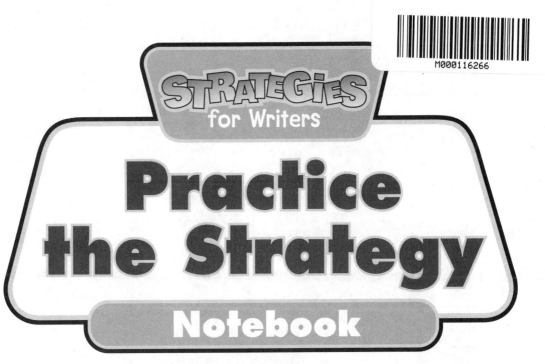

STRATEGIES for Writers

Practice the Strategy

Notebook

Level C

Authors

Leslie W. Crawford, Ed.D.
Georgia College & State University

Rebecca Bowers Sipe, Ed.D.
Eastern Michigan University

Cover Design
Tommaso Design Group

Production by Inkwell Publishing Solutions, Inc.

ISBN 0-7367-1245-3

Zaner-Bloser, Inc., P.O. Box 16764, Columbus, Ohio 43216-6764   (1-800-421-3018)

Printed in the United States of America

05 06 07 08 09 (106) 11 10 9 8 7

NARRATIVE
writing

DESCRIPTIVE
writing

EXPOSITORY
writing

NARRATIVE
writing

PERSUASIVE writing

TEST writing

PreWRiTiNg

Gather
Think about something that I saw or did. Jot notes about my experience.

Read these notes about a time when a writer saw a house being moved.

Topic: Watching a House Being Moved

Notes

- neighbors have cool house

- neighbors wanted to move house to a lake

- watched people move the house last week

- house had to be lifted

- put house on wheels

- truck pulled house down our street

- moved house very slowly

- wires were raised

- didn't hit things along the way

Prewriting

Gather
Think about something that I saw or did. Jot notes about my experience.

your own writing

Now it's your turn to practice this strategy with different topics.
Think of something funny or unusual you once saw.
Who was there? What happened? Where? When?
Why? Jot down some notes about your experience.

Topic:
_____

_____

Notes
_____

_____

_____

_____

_____

_____

_____

_____

_____

_____

RETURN Now go back to Isabel's work on page 19 in the Student Edition.

Prewriting

Organize
Use my notes to make a 5 W's chart.

Now it's time for you to practice this strategy. Look at the notes the writer made on page 6 of this book. Use these notes to complete the 5 W's chart below.

Writer's 5 W's Chart
Who was there?
What happened?
Where did it happen?
When did it happen?
Why did it happen?

PrewRiting

Organize Use my notes to make a 5 W's chart.

your own writing

Now it's time for you to practice this strategy. Look at the notes you made on page 7 of this book. Use your notes to complete the 5 W's chart below.

My 5 W's Chart

Who was there?

What happened?

Where did it happen?

When did it happen?

Why did it happen?

 Now go back to Isabel's work on page 20 in the Student Edition.

Drafting

Write
Draft my personal narrative.
Make sure it has a good beginning.

You know that the beginning of a personal narrative should catch the reader's attention. Read the sentences below. Which one would be the best first sentence, or lead, for a paragraph about moving a house? Circle your answer.

1. I want to tell you about the time a house was moved.

2. Last week, I saw something very unusual.

3. It isn't every day that you see a house rolling down your street!

Look at the one you circled. What kind of lead is it? Is it a surprise lead, a question lead, or a quotation lead?

Now it's time for you to practice this strategy. Look at the 5 W's chart you completed on page 9. Think of three different ways you could begin a personal narrative on that topic. You may want to work with a partner. Write three different leads that would catch the attention of the reader.

Surprise Lead:

_____

_____

Question Lead:

_____

_____

Quotation Lead:

_____

_____

Drafting

Write

Draft my personal narrative.
Make sure it has a good beginning.

Now use this page to begin drafting your own personal narrative using your 5 W's chart on page 9 and the leads you wrote on page 10.

_____

_____

_____

_____

_____

_____

_____

_____

_____

_____

_____

Now go back to Isabel's work on page 22 in the Student Edition.

ReVising

Elaborate   Add interesting details where they are needed.

A personal narrative should give interesting details. Look at the list of interesting details below. These details might be details the writer would want to add to the paragraph to make it more interesting.

It isn't every day that you see a house rolling down your street! That's just what I saw last week, though. Our neighbors. They have a cool, old house. They love the house, but they want to live by a lake. since they could not move the lake, they decided to move there house! We watched the whole project. First, people lifted up the house. Then they put wheels under the house. Next, machines pulled the house to the street. It was hiched to a big truck. Then the truck moved the house very slowly down our street. The movers had to be careful not to hit stuff along the way. The electric and phone wires were raised, too. Then could fit underneath. Can everyone move a house without hiting things along the way These people did!

Read the list of details and put an **X** beside the ones you would add to make the paragraph more interesting.

____ The neighbor's name is Jones.

____ The name of the lake is Lake Huron.

____ My sister and I were watching the house being moved.

____ It takes a truck with three sets of eight wheels to move a house.

ReVising

Elaborate
Add interesting details where they are needed.

_____ It took a tractor-trailer to move the house.

_____ The name of the street is Ferris Street.

_____ The movers had to be careful not to hit mailboxes, streetlights, and fire hydrants.

Now, rewrite the narrative on page 12 adding the interesting details that you checked. You might also want to add interesting details of your own.

_____

_____

_____

_____

_____

_____

_____

_____

_____

_____

Remember:
Use this strategy in
**your own
writing**

Now go back to Isabel's work on page 23 in the Student Edition.

Revising

Clarify

Make sure I used exact words so that my audience can picture everything clearly.

Now it's time for you to practice this strategy. Help the writer paint a clearer word picture for his or her audience. Rewrite each sentence below. Use an exact word from the box to take the place of the underlined word.

workers	slid	beautiful	inched	bulldozers

1. Our neighbors have a <u>cool</u>, old house.

_____

2. First, <u>people</u> lifted up the house.

_____

3. Then they <u>put</u> three sets of eight wheels under the house.

_____

4. Next, <u>machines</u> pulled the house to the street.

_____

5. Then the truck <u>moved</u> the house very slowly down our street.

_____

Remember:
Use this strategy in
your own writing

RETURN
Now go back to Shane's paper on page 24 in the Student Edition.

Narrative Writing • Personal Narrative

Editing

Proofread

Check to see that there are no sentence fragments.

⌐ Indent.
≡ Make a capital.
/ Make a small letter.
∧ Add something.
℮ Take out something.
⊙ Add a period.
⌗ New paragraph
(SP) Spelling error

Now it's time for you to practice this strategy. Here is the revised draft of one writer's personal narrative paragraph. Use the proofreading marks to correct any errors. Use a dictionary to help with spelling.

It isn't every day that you see a house rolling down your street! That's just what I saw last week, though. Our neighbors. They have a beautiful, old house. They love the house, but they want to live by a lake. since they could not move the lake, they decided to move there house! My sister and I watched the whole project. First, workers lifted up the house. Then they slid three sets of eight wheels under the house. Next, bulldozers pulled the house to the street. It was hiched to a big tractor-trailer. Then the truck inched the house very slowly down our street. The movers had to be careful not to hit mailboxes, streetlights, and fire hydrants along the way. The electric and phone wires were raised, too. Then could fit underneath. Can everyone move a house without hiting things along the way These people did!

Remember:
Use this strategy in
your own writing

Now go back to Isabel's work on page 26 in the Student Edition.

Using a Rubric

Use this rubric to assess Isabel's personal narrative on page 27 in your Student Edition. You may work with a partner.

Is there a clear beginning that catches the reader's attention?

Does the narrative tell *who*, *what*, *where*, *when*, and *why*?

Does the paragraph have interesting details?

Do exact words help the reader picture everything clearly?

Is the writing free of sentence fragments?

your own writing

Save this rubric.
Use it to check
your own writing.

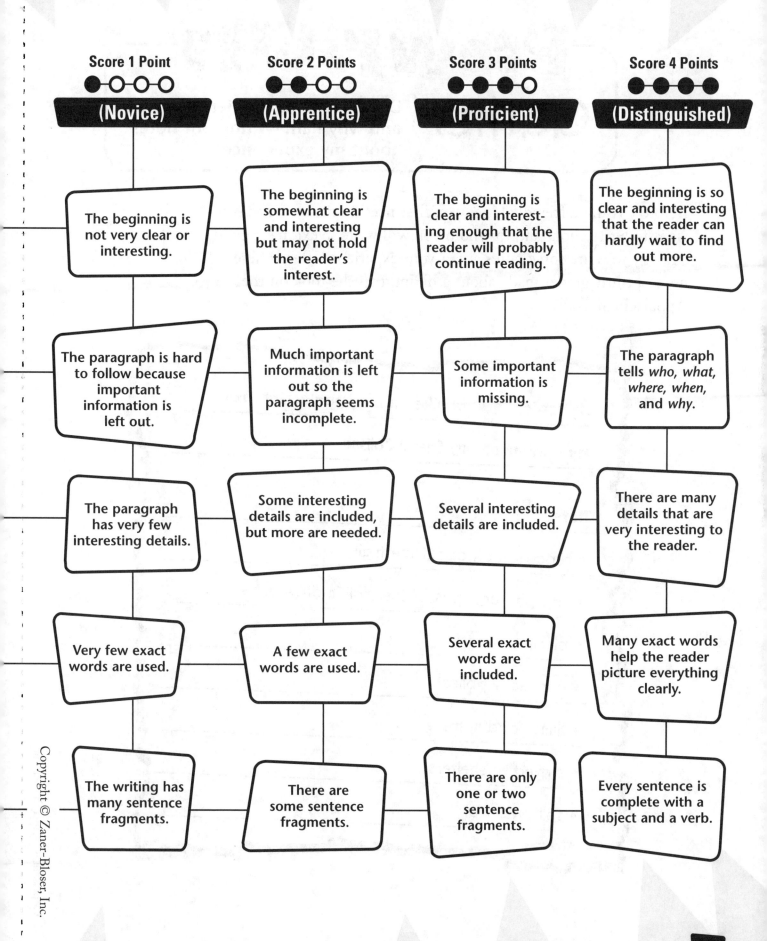

Score 1 Point
●—○—○—○
(Novice)

Score 2 Points
●—●—○—○
(Apprentice)

Score 3 Points
●—●—●—○
(Proficient)

Score 4 Points
●—●—●—●
(Distinguished)

The beginning is not very clear or interesting.

The beginning is somewhat clear and interesting but may not hold the reader's interest.

The beginning is clear and interesting enough that the reader will probably continue reading.

The beginning is so clear and interesting that the reader can hardly wait to find out more.

The paragraph is hard to follow because important information is left out.

Much important information is left out so the paragraph seems incomplete.

Some important information is missing.

The paragraph tells *who*, *what*, *where*, *when*, and *why*.

The paragraph has very few interesting details.

Some interesting details are included, but more are needed.

Several interesting details are included.

There are many details that are very interesting to the reader.

Very few exact words are used.

A few exact words are used.

Several exact words are included.

Many exact words help the reader picture everything clearly.

The writing has many sentence fragments.

There are some sentence fragments.

There are only one or two sentence fragments.

Every sentence is complete with a subject and a verb.

Prewriting

Gather

Decide who my audience will be and why I am writing. Jot notes about my experience.

Before writing a friendly letter, you first need to decide what you want to write about and to whom you will write. Next, it's a good strategy to write some notes about your experience. Read these notes a third-grader made about a hiking trip she took on the Appalachian Trail.

My topic: my hike on the Appalachian Trail

My audience: my friend Jalissa

Notes

- read a book about the trail
- saw photographs of the trail in different states
- planned our trip
- packed supplies
- hung food in trees
- stayed at shelters
- followed trail

PReWRiTiNg

Gather

Decide who my audience will be and why I am writing. Jot notes about my experience.

Now it's your turn to practice this strategy with different topics. Think about an outdoor adventure you once had. Where did you go? What did you see? What did you do? Decide who might like to receive a letter about your adventure. Then jot down some notes about your experience.

My topic: _____

My audience: _____

Notes: _____

_____

_____

_____

_____

_____

_____

_____

_____

 Now go back to Justin's work on page 37 in the Student Edition.

Narrative Writing • Friendly Letter

Prewriting

Organize

Use my notes to make a sequence chain.

your own writing

Now it's time for you to practice this strategy. Look at the notes you made on page 19 of this book. Think about the order in which events happened. Then use your notes to make a sequence chain.

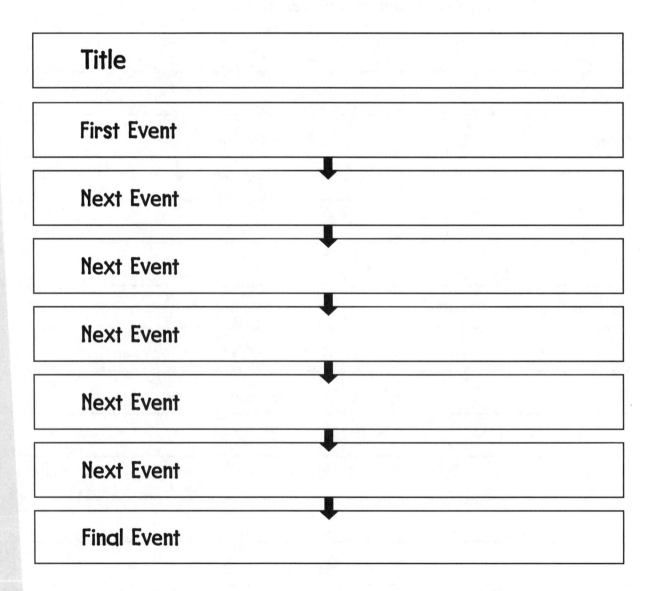

| Title |
| First Event |
| Next Event |
| Next Event |
| Next Event |
| Next Event |
| Next Event |
| Final Event |

RETURN Now go back to Justin's work on page 38 in the Student Edition.

Drafting

Write
Draft my friendly letter. Be sure I include all five letter parts.

your own writing

Now it's time for you to practice this strategy. Look at the audience you named on page 19 of this book. Write a heading, a greeting, a draft of the body of your letter, a closing, and your name as you would write them in a letter to this person. Remember to use capital letters and commas correctly.

heading _____

_____

_____

_____ greeting

body

_____

_____

_____

_____

_____

closing _____

signature _____

RETURN
Now go back to Justin's paper on page 40 in the Student Edition.

ReVising

Elaborate

Add details that will be especially interesting to my audience.

Now it's time for you to practice this strategy. First, read this draft of part of Elena's letter. You will see some mistakes. You can fix them now or later.

I wish you could of come hiking with us on the Appalachian Trail!

Did you know that the trail goes all the way from Georgia to maine

The whole trail is very long, but we hiked only a small part in Georgia.

We had to plan carefully before we left. We needed lots of supplies,

but I had to make sure that my pack wasn't too heavy to carry.

Mom and I took a lot of stuff.

We started at Springer Mountain. We didn't get lost because we

Revising

Elaborate

Add details that will be especially interesting to my audience.

followed the trail. Sometimes the trail was steep, and I got tired.

Luckily, their were shelters along the way. They were good spots to

rest, to eat, or to sleep at nite.

Read the details below. Elena thought she might add some of these to her draft. Circle the three that are most interesting and give the most information. Then go back and add them to Elena's letter where you think they belong. You may have to cross out some words in the draft when you add the new details.

Details

- The trail is about 2,160 miles.
- I slept really well at night.
- We took a map, a tent, food, water, clothes, safety equipment, and sleeping bags.
- There were white paint markings along the trail.
- I ate a lot of food every day we hiked.

Remember: Use this strategy in your own writing

Now go back to Justin's work on page 41 in the Student Edition.

ReVising

Clarify

Make sure my letter has my voice and sounds like me.

Elena read her letter to herself. She decided to change this sentence so that it sounded more personal.

Sometimes the trail was steep, and I got tired. ∧ so that my legs felt like spaghetti ∧

Now it's time for you to practice this strategy. Think about the notes you took about your own outdoor adventure. Read each sentence below. Rewrite each sentence so that it tells about your adventure and sounds more personal. Give each sentence a stronger voice by telling what you thought or felt.

1. I had fun on the trip.

_____

_____

2. We saw interesting things.

_____

_____

3. We did exciting things.

_____

_____

4. I liked the animals.

_____

_____

Remember: Use this strategy in **your own writing**

Now go back to Justin's work on page 42 in the Student Edition.

24

Narrative Writing • Friendly Letter

Copyright © Zaner-Bloser, Inc.

Editing

Proofread
Check to see that I've used capital letters and commas correctly.

Proofreading Marks	
⊐ Indent.	ℓ Take out something.
≡ Make a capital.	⊙ Add a period.
/ Make a small letter.	⌗ New paragraph
∧ Add something.	ⓈⓅ Spelling error

Now it's time for you to practice this strategy. Here is the revised draft of Elena's letter. Use the proofreading marks to correct any errors.

45 Rocky Ridge Lane

Jasper, GA 30143

May 3 2002

dear Jalissa

    I wish you could of come hiking with us on the Appalachian Trail! Did you know that the trail goes all the way from Georgia to maine The whole trail is about 2,160 miles long, but we hiked only a small part in Georgia.

    We had to plan carefully before we left. We needed lots of supplies, but I had to make sure that my pack wasn't too heavy to carry. Mom and I took a map, a tent, food, water, clothes, safety equipment, and sleeping bags.

    We started at Springer Mountain. We didn't get lost because we followed white paint markings along the trail. Sometimes the trail was steep, and I got so tired that my legs felt like spaghetti. Luckily, their were shelters along the way. They were good spots to rest, to eat, or to sleep at nite.

love

Elena

Remember: Use this strategy in **your own writing**

Now go back to page 44 in the Student Edition.

Using a Rubric

Use this rubric to score Justin's letter on page 45 in your Student Edition. You may work with a partner.

Does the writer tell who the reader of the letter will be? Is the purpose of the letter clear?

Are the events told in the order in which they happened?

Does the letter include interesting details?

Does the letter sound personal? Can you hear the writer's "voice"?

Are all five letter parts included, written correctly, and punctuated correctly?

your own writing

Save this rubric. Use it to check your own writing.

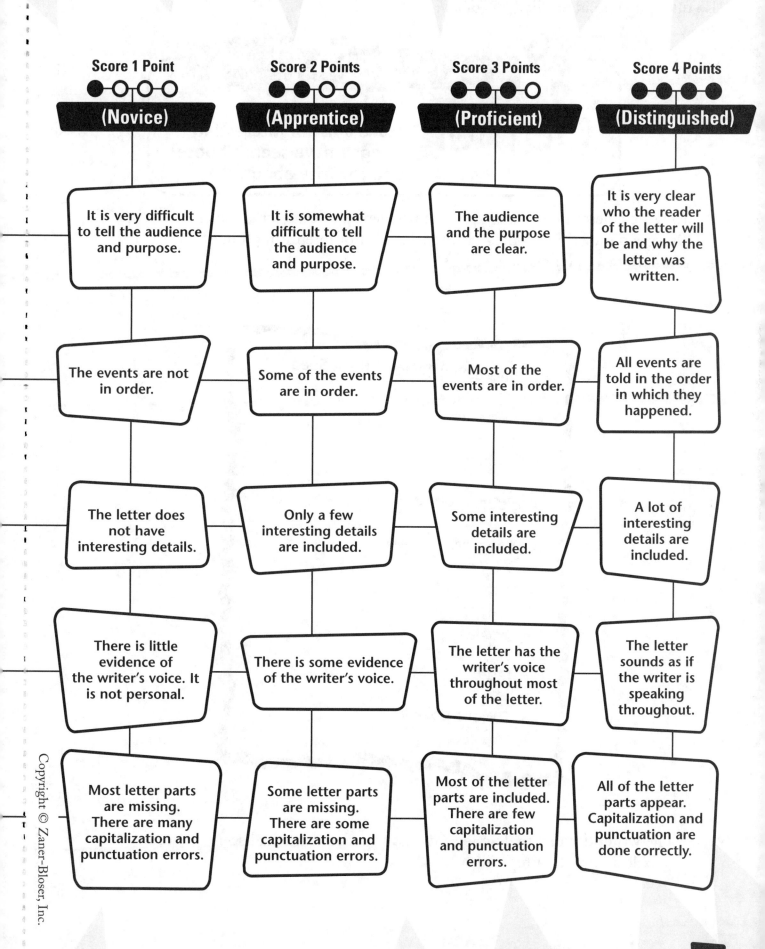

Score 1 Point
(Novice)

It is very difficult to tell the audience and purpose.

The events are not in order.

The letter does not have interesting details.

There is little evidence of the writer's voice. It is not personal.

Most letter parts are missing. There are many capitalization and punctuation errors.

Score 2 Points
(Apprentice)

It is somewhat difficult to tell the audience and purpose.

Some of the events are in order.

Only a few interesting details are included.

There is some evidence of the writer's voice.

Some letter parts are missing. There are some capitalization and punctuation errors.

Score 3 Points
(Proficient)

The audience and the purpose are clear.

Most of the events are in order.

Some interesting details are included.

The letter has the writer's voice throughout most of the letter.

Most of the letter parts are included. There are few capitalization and punctuation errors.

Score 4 Points
(Distinguished)

It is very clear who the reader of the letter will be and why the letter was written.

All events are told in the order in which they happened.

A lot of interesting details are included.

The letter sounds as if the writer is speaking throughout.

All of the letter parts appear. Capitalization and punctuation are done correctly.

Prewriting

Gather

Make a list of interesting things I have seen. Choose one to write about.

To write a descriptive paragraph, you first have to decide on a topic. One good prewriting strategy is to make a list of interesting things you have seen. Here is one writer's list.

Interesting Things I Have Seen

- ice statue

- volcano

- gigantic pizza

- dinosaur skeleton

- space shuttle

- geysers

- tea ceremony

- famous painting

The writer decided to describe a dinosaur skeleton she had seen. She drew a circle around that topic idea.

Prewriting

Gather

Make a list of interesting things I have seen. Choose one to write about.

your own writing

Now it's your turn to practice this strategy with a different topic. What interesting things have you seen? Think about what you've seen in your neighborhood, in your town, or on a trip. Write down some topic ideas. Which one do you think a reader would find most interesting? Circle it.

Interesting Things I Have Seen

1. _____

2. _____

3. _____

4. _____

5. _____

6. _____

7. _____

8. _____

9. _____

10. _____

RETURN

Now go back to Ramon's work on page 57 in the Student Edition.

Descriptive Writing • Descriptive Paragraph **29**

Prewriting

Organize

Use what I know about my topic to make an observation chart.

Look at the topic idea that the writer circled on page 28 of this book. Then look at the observation chart below. The writer organized information about the dinosaur skeleton by as many of the senses as she could use. Since she couldn't really hear or touch the dinosaur, she imagined what it might be like and put that on her chart.

Topic	Dinosaur Skeleton			
Sight	**Sound**	**Touch**	**Taste**	**Smell**
huge	loud	hard		
shiny brown	ground thumping	jagged		
big eye holes	leaves brushing	bumpy		
pointed teeth		pointed		
smooth bones				

Descriptive Writing • Descriptive Paragraph

Prewriting

Organize

Use what I know about my topic to make an observation chart.

your own writing

Now it's time for you to practice this strategy. Look at the topic idea you circled on page 29 of this book. Think about how the subject you chose looks, sounds, feels, tastes, and smells. Record your observations on the chart below. Use as many senses as apply to your topic.

My Topic				
Sight	**Sound**	**Touch**	**Taste**	**Smell**

RETURN Now go back to Ramon's work on page 58 in the Student Edition.

Drafting

Write

Draft my paragraph. Make sure it has an interesting topic sentence that tells the main idea.

A descriptive paragraph needs an interesting topic sentence that tells what the paragraph is about. Read the sentences below. Which one would be the best topic sentence for a descriptive paragraph about a dinosaur skeleton? Circle your answer.

1. Its back has a strange shape.

2. I am staring at an awesome dinosaur skeleton.

3. I like going to museums.

your own writing

Now it's time for you to practice this strategy. Look at your observation chart on page 31. Try to draft three different topic sentences to begin a paragraph that describes your topic. Put a check mark beside the topic sentence you like best.

Topic Sentence 1

_____

_____

Topic Sentence 2

_____

_____

Topic Sentence 3

_____

_____

Descriptive Writing • Descriptive Paragraph

Drafting

Write

Draft my paragraph. Make sure it has an interesting topic sentence that tells the main idea.

Look at the topic sentence you chose on page 32. Begin your own descriptive paragraph using this topic sentence.

_____

_____

_____

_____

_____

_____

_____

_____

_____

_____

_____

 Now go back to Ramon's work on page 60 in the Student Edition.

Descriptive Writing • Descriptive Paragraph

Use after page 60 in the Student Edition.

ReVising

Elaborate Look for places to use exact adjectives.

Now it's time for you to practice this strategy. Help the writer use more exact adjectives. Rewrite each sentence below. Use exact adjectives from the box to take the place of the underlined word in each sentence.

Exact Adjectives

deep	Field Museum
brown	dozens of pointed

1. Now Sue is in the <u>museum</u> in Chicago.

   _____

2. Her shiny, <u>dark</u> bones are held together by small pieces of metal.

   _____

3. There are <u>big</u> holes in the skull where her nose and eyes once were.

   _____

4. She has <u>many</u> teeth that could rip through meat and crush bones.

   _____

   _____

Descriptive Writing • Descriptive Paragraph

ReVising

Elaborate
Look for places to use exact adjectives.

Read the following sentences and decide which word or words could be replaced with more exact adjectives. Underline the word or words. Then, rewrite each sentence using adjectives of your own choosing. Add or take out words necessary to complete your new sentence.

1. You can see many old skeletons and artifacts in a museum.

_____

_____

2. I saw both big and small dinosaur skeletons.

_____

3. I like to study the different bones.

_____

4. Can you imagine the noisy sounds the dinosaurs might have made?

_____

_____

5. It's fun to look at the hard bones, but we should not touch!

_____

_____

Remember: Use this strategy in **your own writing**

Now go back to Ramon's work on page 61 in the Student Edition.

Descriptive Writing • Descriptive Paragraph

ReVising

Clarify

Take out details that don't tell about the topic.

Now it's time for you to practice this strategy. Here is a draft of the descriptive paragraph about the dinosaur skeleton. Draw a line through the three sentences that don't tell about the main idea. Don't worry about fixing other mistakes right now.

I am staring at an awesome dinosaur skeleton. it is the largest Tyrannosaurus rex skeleton ever found. Do you know the dinosaur's name. It is called Sue, after the woman who found the dinosaur's bones. I would like to hunt for dinosaur bones someday, too. Now Sue is in the Field Museum in chicago. Her shiny, brown bones are held together by small pieces of metal. There are deep holes in the skull where her nose and eyes once were. She has dozens of pointed teeth that could rip through meat and crush bones. Sue's back bends like the letter S. That's the first letter in my name! Her smooth, round ribs curve down toward the floor. she has two short arms, and she stands on two powerful legs. Each foot has three long toes and sharp klaws. Some cats have six toes on a paw. Sue's enormous tail stretches out to the right in the air behind her In all, she is forty-one feet long from her noze to the end of her tail. Sue crouches as if she is ready to pounce. What a relief that she can't pounce on me!

Remember: Use this strategy in **your own writing**

 Now go back to Ramon's work on page 62 in the Student Edition.

Editing

Proofread
Check that every sentence begins with a capital letter and ends with the correct punctuation mark.

⌐ Indent.
≡ Make a capital.
╱ Make a small letter.
∧ Add something.
℮ Take out something.
⊙ Add a period.
New paragraph
SP Spelling error

Now it's time for you to practice this strategy. Here is a revised draft of the descriptive paragraph about the dinosaur skeleton. Use the proofreading marks to correct the errors. Use a dictionary to help with spelling.

I am staring at an awesome dinosaur skeleton. it is the largest Tyrannosaurus rex skeleton ever found. Do you know the dinosaur's name. It is called Sue, after the woman who found the dinosaur's bones. Now Sue is in the Field Museum in chicago. Her shiny, brown bones are held together by small pieces of metal. There are deep holes in the skull where her nose and eyes once were. She has dozens of pointed teeth that could rip through meat and crush bones. Sue's back bends like the letter *S.* Her smooth, round ribs curve down toward the floor. she has two short arms, and she stands on two powerful legs. Each foot has three long toes and sharp klaws. Sue's enormous tail stretches out to the right in the air behind her In all, she is forty-one feet long from her noze to the end of her tail. Sue crouches as if she is ready to pounce. What a relief that she can't pounce on me!

Remember:
Use this strategy in
**your own
writing**

Now go back to Ramon's work on page 64 in the Student Edition.

Using a Rubric

Use this rubric to assess Ramon's descriptive paragraph on page 65 in your Student Edition. You may work with a partner.

Is there an interesting topic sentence that tells the reader the main idea of the paragraph?

Does the writer use as many of the five senses as he can to tell about the object? Is the information in logical order?

Does the paragraph use exact adjectives to tell about the topic?

Does every sentence tell about the main idea?

Does every sentence begin with a capital letter and end with the correct punctuation mark?

your own writing

Save this rubric. Use it to check your own writing.

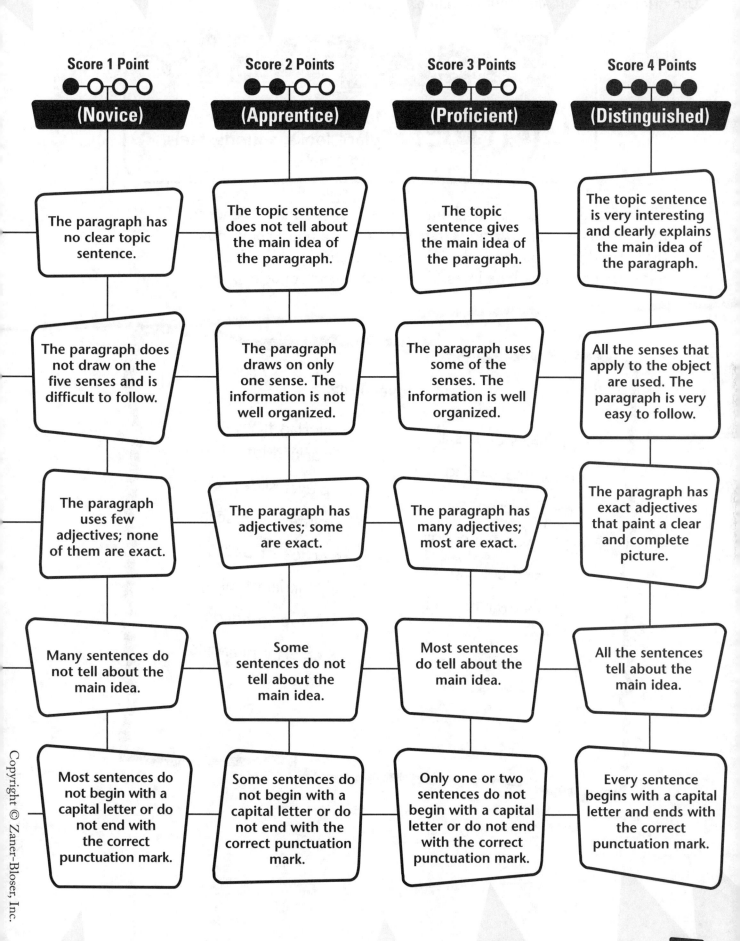

Score 1 Point
(Novice)

Score 2 Points
(Apprentice)

Score 3 Points
(Proficient)

Score 4 Points
(Distinguished)

The paragraph has no clear topic sentence.

The topic sentence does not tell about the main idea of the paragraph.

The topic sentence gives the main idea of the paragraph.

The topic sentence is very interesting and clearly explains the main idea of the paragraph.

The paragraph does not draw on the five senses and is difficult to follow.

The paragraph draws on only one sense. The information is not well organized.

The paragraph uses some of the senses. The information is well organized.

All the senses that apply to the object are used. The paragraph is very easy to follow.

The paragraph uses few adjectives; none of them are exact.

The paragraph has adjectives; some are exact.

The paragraph has many adjectives; most are exact.

The paragraph has exact adjectives that paint a clear and complete picture.

Many sentences do not tell about the main idea.

Some sentences do not tell about the main idea.

Most sentences do tell about the main idea.

All the sentences tell about the main idea.

Most sentences do not begin with a capital letter or do not end with the correct punctuation mark.

Some sentences do not begin with a capital letter or do not end with the correct punctuation mark.

Only one or two sentences do not begin with a capital letter or do not end with the correct punctuation mark.

Every sentence begins with a capital letter and ends with the correct punctuation mark.

Prewriting

Gather

Jot notes that tell how the place looks, sounds, feels, and smells.

To write a descriptive essay about a place, first you have to choose the place. A good prewriting strategy is to write notes about how that place looks, sounds, feels, and smells. Here are one writer's notes about a ballpark he loves. Read what she wrote below.

Glover Park

- pitcher stands still
- umpire's booming voice
- crowd screams
- sticky cotton candy
- slurping cold sodas
- players run around bases
- pressing crowds at entrance
- ball zooms

- blaring tunes in parking lot
- player slides
- buttery popcorn
- crack of bat
- stomping feet
- clapping hands
- colorful pennants at gates

Use after page 74 in the Student Edition.

Prewriting

Gather

Jot notes that tell how the place looks, sounds, feels, and smells.

your own writing

Now it's your turn to practice this strategy with different topics. Think of an interesting place that you have visited. What did you see, hear, feel, taste, or smell? Write down the name of the place. Then jot down some details that describe it.

Place: _____

_____

Notes: _____

_____

_____

_____

_____

_____

_____

_____

_____

_____

_____

_____

 RETURN Now go back to Damara's work on page 75 in the Student Edition.

Descriptive Writing • Descriptive Essay

Prewriting

Organize

Use my notes to make a spider map.

Now it's time for you to practice this strategy. Now you can practice making a spider map. Use the information about Glover Park on page 40 and organize it into a spider map. You have seen spider maps organized in different ways. The model essay was organized by senses. Damara organized her spider map by her favorite things. You can organize this map by location. On the lines of the legs, organize the information from the chart. You may or may not use all of the lines coming from the legs. You may have to draw more.

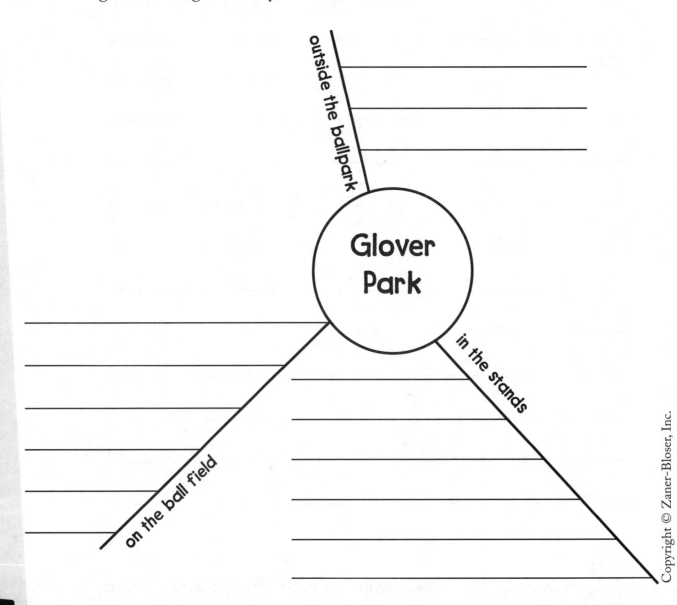

Descriptive Writing • Descriptive Essay

Prewriting

Organize

Use my notes to make a spider map.

your own writing

Look at the notes you wrote on page 41 of this book. Think about how you can organize your notes on a spider map. Use the spider map below to organize your notes into topics. You may not need to use all of the lines on each leg. You may need to draw more lines on one or more of the legs.

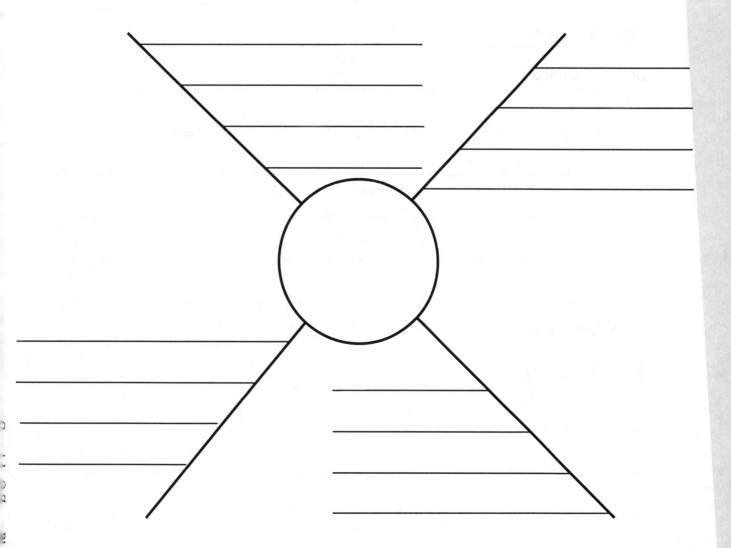

RETURN

Now go back to Damara's work on page 76 in the Student Edition.

Drafting

Write

Draft my essay. Write a topic sentence for each paragraph. Write detail sentences for every topic sentence.

your own writing

Now it's time for you to practice this strategy. Look at the spider map you made on page 43. Write a topic sentence for each leg of your spider. Each topic sentence should tell the main idea of a paragraph in your draft. Add three detail sentences for each topic sentence.

Topic Sentence 1: _____

Detail Sentences: _____

_____

_____

_____

_____

_____

Topic Sentence 2: _____

Detail Sentences: _____

_____

_____

_____

_____

Drafting

Write

Draft my essay. Write a topic sentence for each paragraph. Write detail sentences for every topic sentence.

Topic Sentence 3:

_____

Detail Sentences:

_____

_____

_____

_____

_____

_____

Topic Sentence 4:

_____

Detail Sentences:

_____

_____

_____

_____

_____

_____

 Now go back to Damara's work on page 78 in the Student Edition.

Descriptive Writing • Descriptive Essay

ReVising

Elaborate
Add details that compare one thing to another.

The writer of this draft needs help making comparisons. Help the writer by drawing a line to match the person or thing in Column 1 with what it could be compared to in Column 2.

Person or Thing	Comparison
• how the pitcher looks	• like a rocket
• the way the ball zooms	• as loud as a roaring train
• how the cotton candy looks	• like pink clouds
• how the people sound	• like a statue

Now take the items you matched and write sentences joining them together.

Example: The pitcher looks like a statue.

_____

_____

_____

ReVising

Elaborate
Add details that compare one thing to another.

Now it's time for you to practice this strategy. Find the information in Column 1 in the essay. Take a phrase from Column 2 and see where it fits in the writer's draft.

Add the four comparisons to this part of one writer's draft. Adding these comparisons will make the writer's essay clearer and more interesting. Use a caret (^) to show where the new words belong. Draw a line through any words that are no longer needed. (You might see some errors. You can fix them or let them go until later.)

A lot happens. It happens on the field. Sometimes the pitcher stands

perfectly still. He looks stiff. Then the ball zooms toward home plate.

You hear the crack of the bat. The ball sails into the air. Runners zip

around the bases. One player slides. The dirt flies. The umpire's voice

booms. The player is safe. Colored lights flash. The lights are on the

scoreboard.

A lot happens in the stands, too. People sell snacks. The sticky cotton

candy looks pretty. Children slurp cold sodas. You can smell buttery

popcorn. The fans scream when their team scores a run. Some people

stomp their feet. Others clap their hands. Together, they sound loud.

Remember: Use this strategy in **your own writing**

Now go back to Damara's work on page 79 in the Student Edition.

ReVising

Clarify   Combine short, choppy sentences.

Now it's time for you to practice this strategy. Here are some sentences from the descriptive essay about the ballpark. Help the writer combine some short, choppy sentences. Write each new sentence on the lines.

1. A lot happens. It happens on the field.

   _____

2. The ball sails into the air. Runners zip around the bases.

   _____

3. One player slides. The dirt flies.

   _____

4. Colored lights flash. The lights are on the scoreboard.

   _____

5. You will enjoy this ballpark. This ballpark is great.

   _____

Remember: Use this strategy in your own writing

RETURN   Now go back to Damara's work on page 80 in the Student Edition.

48   **Descriptive Writing** • Descriptive Essay

Editing

Proofread

Check that the main parts of each compound sentence are joined with a comma and a joining word.

	Indent.		Take out something.
	Make a capital.		Add a period.
	Make a small letter.		New paragraph
	Add something.	SP	Spelling error

Now it's time for you to practice this strategy. Here is part of one writer's revised draft of the descriptive essay about the ballpark. Use the proofreading marks to correct the errors. Use a dictionary to help with spelling.

Glover Park

If you like baseball, Glover Park is the best plase to be on a summer day. You see the players up close everyone feels the excitement.

As you get close to the stadium, you can see the colorful pennants of all of the teams flying around the gates. From the parking lot you can hear familiar tunes blaring from the loud speaker. People press close as they enter the gates.

A lot happens. It happens on the field. Sometimes the pitcher stands perfectly still. He looks like a statue. Then the ball zooms like a rocket toward home plate. You hear the crack of the bat. The ball sails into the air. Runners zip around the bases. One player slides. The dirt flies. The umpire's voice booms. The player is safe. Colored lights flash. The lights are on the scoreboard.

I know you will enjoy this great ballpark everyone always has a good time there!

Remember: Use this strategy in **your own writing**

Now go back to Damara's work on page 82 in the Student Edition.

Using a Rubric

Use this rubric to assess Damara's descriptive essay on page 83 in your Student Edition. You may work with a partner.

Audience

Does the writer's description clearly put the reader in the place being described?

Organization

Does each paragraph have a topic sentence to tell the reader what the paragraph is about? Do detail sentences tell about the topic sentence?

Elaboration

How well does the writer use comparisons to add to the description?

Clarification

Have short, choppy sentences been combined?

your own writing

Save this rubric. Use it to check your own writing.

Conventions & Skills

Are the parts of compound sentences correctly joined with a comma and a joining word such as *and, but,* or *or*?

Score 1 Point
● ○ ○ ○
(Novice)

Score 2 Points
● ● ○ ○
(Apprentice)

Score 3 Points
● ● ● ○
(Proficient)

Score 4 Points
● ● ● ●
(Distinguished)

The essay does not tell how the place looks, sounds, feels, or smells. The reader does not get a sense of the place.

The essay has some description, but not enough to put the reader in the place.

There is a lot of description so the reader gets a good idea of the place.

The writer clearly tells how the place looks, sounds, feels, and smells. The reader feels as if he or she is in the place.

It is hard to tell what each paragraph is about.

Some of the sentences in each paragraph tell about the same topic.

Most paragraphs have a clear topic sentence and detail sentences that support it.

Every paragraph has a clear topic sentence and good detail sentences that support it.

The writer does not use comparisons.

The writer uses few comparisons.

The writer makes some interesting comparisons.

Several comparisons paint clear, interesting word pictures.

There are many short, choppy sentences.

There are some short, choppy sentences.

There are few short, choppy sentences.

There are no short, choppy sentences. The writing is smooth.

Many compound sentences are written incorrectly.

A few compound sentences are written incorrectly.

Most compound sentences are written correctly.

All compound sentences are written correctly.

Prewriting

Gather

Make a list of everything the reader will need to do the project.

One writer chose to write a how-to essay about washing a car. She and her friends at school wash cars on the weekends and donate the money to their favorite charities. She wants to write a how-to essay so her friends at other schools can learn how to do the same thing. The first thing the writer does is make a list of the materials needed to wash a car. She doesn't want to leave anything out. Read her list below.

Topic: How to Wash a Car

Materials:

- Sponge
- Pail
- Special car soap
- Soapy water
- Old towels

Prewriting

Gather

Make a list of everything the reader will need to do the project.

your own writing

Now it's time to practice this strategy with different topics. What are you an expert at doing or making? Could you teach your classmates how to:

• feed a pet;

• make a bed;

• clean a closet?

Choose something that you can teach others. Then make a list of everything someone would need to complete your project.

Topic:

Materials:

_____

_____

_____

_____

_____

_____

_____

_____

RETURN
Now go back to Meg's work on page 95 in the Student Edition.

Prewriting

Organize

Use the items in my list to make a sequence chain.

The writer must now take the items in her list to make a sequence chain. First she looked at the list of materials she made. Then she completed the sequence chain so she would be sure to keep her steps in order. Read how she completed her sequence chain below.

Sequence Chain

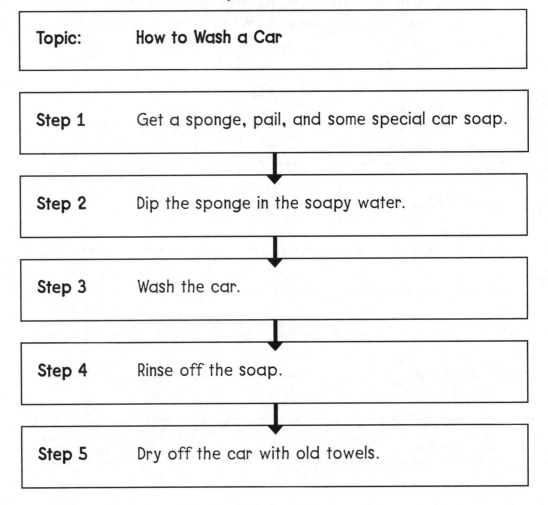

Topic:	How to Wash a Car
Step 1	Get a sponge, pail, and some special car soap.
Step 2	Dip the sponge in the soapy water.
Step 3	Wash the car.
Step 4	Rinse off the soap.
Step 5	Dry off the car with old towels.

Prewriting

Organize
Use the items in my list to make a sequence chain.

your own writing

Now it's your turn to practice this strategy. Look at the list of materials you made on page 53 of this book. Use the list to help you fill in the sequence chain below. Remember that the chain should show the steps of your how-to project in order. If your project doesn't have five steps, leave some of the spaces blank.

Sequence Chain

Topic:

Step 1

↓

Step 2

↓

Step 3

↓

Step 4

↓

Step 5

RETURN

Now go back to Meg's work on page 96 in the Student Edition.

Expository Writing • How-To Essay

Drafting

Write
Draft my essay by separating the steps in the sequence chain into paragraphs.

Next the writer must take the items in the sequence chain and start drafting her essay. She knows the items she wants to include and the order they should be in. Here is part of her essay.

Get a sponge, a pail, and some special car soap.

Dip the sponge in the soapy water.

Your ready to start washing the car. Wash one section

of the car. Rinse off the soap.

your own writing

Now it's your turn to practice this strategy. Look at the sequence chain you made on page 55. Draft a paragraph for Step 1 in your chain. Then draft paragraphs for Steps 2 through 5.

Remember that all the sentences in a paragraph should explain what someone needs to do to complete that step. Indent the first line of each paragraph.

Step 1 _____

_____

_____

_____

Step 2 _____

_____

_____

Drafting

Write

Draft my essay by separating the steps in the sequence chain into paragraphs.

Step 3

_____

_____

_____

_____

Step 4

_____

_____

_____

_____

Step 5

_____

_____

_____

_____

 Now go back to Meg's work on page 98 in the Student Edition.

ReVising

Elaborate

Add information to fill in gaps in my how-to essay.

Now it's your turn to practice this strategy. After the first draft was finished, the writer reread the essay. She discovered that some important information was missing.

The following words and sentences include information the writer could use to fill in gaps in her essay. Decide where you think these words and sentences belong and add them to the draft. Use a caret (^) to show where each belongs. Don't worry about fixing other mistakes in this draft. You will fix them later.

1. a hose

2. Put the right amounts of soap and cool water in the pail.

3. Connect the hose to a faucet.

4. Wash and rinse the rest of the car, one section at a time.

    One of my faverite ways two help charities is washing cars.

Its not very hard and it can also be fun. Here is what you have

to do.

    Get a sponge, a pail, and some special car soap. Dip the

sponge in the soapy water.

    Your ready to start washing the car. Wash one section of the

car. Use a hose to rinse off the soap.

ReVising

Elaborate

Add information to fill in gaps in my how-to essay.

Reread the writer's draft, including the words and sentences you added. On the following lines, write why you chose to place the added information where you did.

Sentence 1: _____

_____

_____

Sentence 2: _____

_____

_____

Sentence 3: _____

_____

_____

Sentence 4: _____

_____

_____

Remember: Use this strategy in **your own writing**

Now go back to Meg's work on page 99 in the Student Edition.

ReVising

Clarify

Use time-order words to make the order of the steps clear.

Now it's your turn to practice this strategy. Here are some time-order words that might be added to the writer's draft, or to your own draft.

Time-Order Words

Next	First	Last
Second	Then	Now

Use these words (or your own time-order words) to help the writer make the order of the steps clearer in this part of her paper. You may need to use words more than one time. Use a caret (^) to show where each time-order word belongs. Correct the capitalization when you put in the new words, but don't worry about fixing other mistakes in this draft. You will fix them later.

Get a sponge, a pail, a hose, and some special car soap. Put the right amounts of soap and cool water in the pail. Dip the sponge in the soapy water. Connect the hose to a faucet.

Your ready to start washing the car. Wash one section of the car. Use a hose to rinse off the soap. Wash and rinse the rest of the car, one section at a time.

The car is almost ready to go. They're is one more thing to do. Dry the car off with old towels. Your customer will drive away with a shiney, clean car. You will feel good about working and having fun all for a good cause.

Remember: Use this strategy in **your own writing**

 Now go back to Meg's work on page 100 in the Student Edition.

⊐ Indent.	ℓ Take out something.
≡ Make a capital.	⊙ Add a period.
/ Make a small letter.	⌗ New paragraph
∧ Add something.	SP Spelling error

Editing
Proofread
Check that each homophone fits its meaning.

Now it's your turn to practice this strategy. Here is the revised draft of the writer's how-to essay. Use the proofreading marks to correct the errors. Use a dictionary to help with spelling.

One of my faverite ways two help charities is washing cars. How does washing cars help charities? My classmates and I wash the neighborhood cars one Saturday a month, and we donate the money to charity. Its not very hard and it can also be fun. Here is what you have to do.

First, get a sponge, a pail, a hose, and some special car soap. Second, put the right amounts of soap and cool water in the pail. Next, dip the sponge in soapy water. Then, connect the hose to a faucet.

Now, your ready to start washing the car. Wash one section of the car. Then, use a hose to rinse off the soap. Now, wash and rinse the rest of the car, one section at a time.

The car is almost ready to go. They're is one more thing to do. Last, dry the car off with towels. Your customer will drive away with a shiney, clean car. You will feel good about working and having fun all for a good cause.

Remember: Use this strategy in **your own writing**

 RETURN Now go back to Meg's work on page 102 in the Student Edition.

Expository Writing • How-To Essay

61

Using a Rubric

Use this rubric to assess Meg's how-to essay on page 103 in your Student Edition. You may work with a partner.

Audience
Does the essay tell the reader exactly what materials are needed to complete the project?

Organization
Are the how-to steps told in order?

Elaboration
Is every step given? Is the information for each step complete?

Clarification
Do time-order words make the order of the steps clear?

your own writing

Save this rubric. Use it to check your own writing.

Conventions & Skills
When choosing homophones, does the writer use the correct one?

Score 1 Point	Score 2 Points	Score 3 Points	Score 4 Points
(Novice)	**(Apprentice)**	**(Proficient)**	**(Distinguished)**
The essay does not mention most of the materials the reader will need.	The essay mentions a few of the materials the reader will need.	Most of the materials the reader will need are mentioned.	All the materials the reader will need are mentioned.
Many steps are told out of order.	A few steps are told out of order.	Most steps are told in order.	All the steps are told in order.
Many steps are missing or give incomplete information.	Some steps are missing or give incomplete information.	Most steps are given with complete information.	Complete information is given for every step.
There are no time-order words.	A few time-order words help make the order of the steps clear.	Some time-order words help make the order of the steps clear.	Time-order words clearly lead the reader from step to step.
Many homophones are used incorrectly.	A few homophones are used incorrectly.	Most homophones are used correctly.	All the homophones are used correctly.

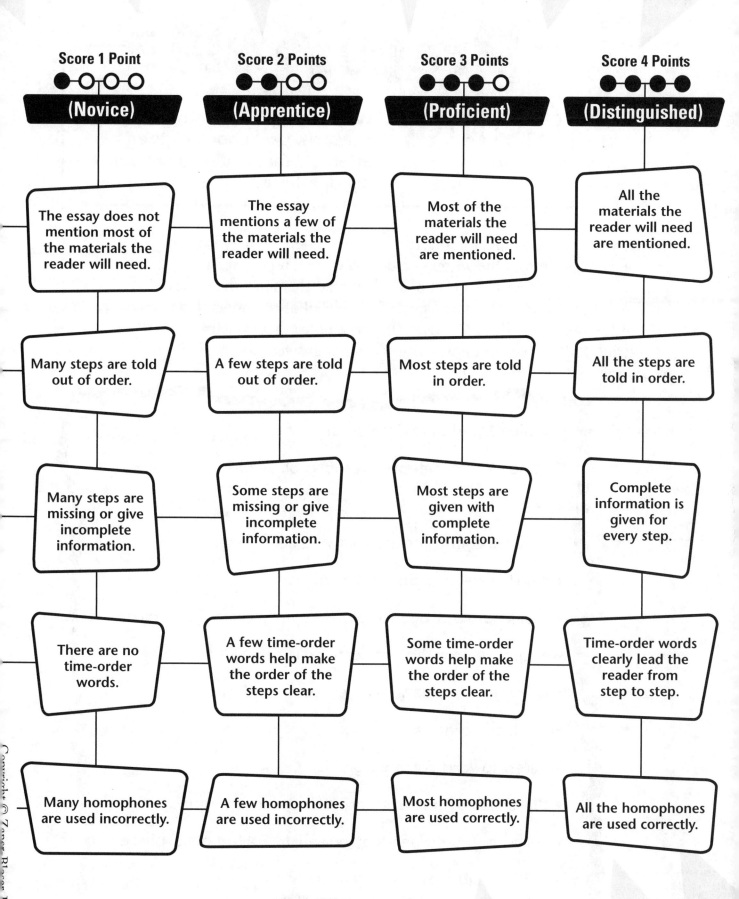

PReWRiTiNg

Gather

Write two questions to guide my research. Use a book or the Internet. Take notes to answer my questions.

After you choose a topic for a factual report, a good strategy is to write two questions. One writer decided to write a report about meteors. Read the writer's questions. Then read the notes the writer made. After you read the notes, put a **1** beside all of the notes that go with **Question 1**. Put a **2** beside all of the notes that go with **Question 2**. If a piece of information does not answer either question, put an **X** beside it.

Question 1: What are meteors?

Question 2: Do meteors ever land on Earth?

Notes:

- once thought to come from weather changes

- usually small and don't hit Earth

- chunks of rock and metal that usually come from comets

- larger meteors that hit Earth called meteorites

- called meteoroids when they go around sun

- can make craters

- pulled toward Earth by gravity

- thousands of small meteorites found in Antarctica

- called meteors when they come into Earth's atmosphere

- get hot and glow

PrewRitiNg

Gather

Write two questions to guide my research. Use a book or the Internet. Take notes to answer my questions.

your own writing

Now it's your turn to practice this strategy with different topics. Think of something you would like to know more about. Have you ever wondered how something works or how something is made? Maybe you'd like to learn about a famous person, an interesting place, or an unusual animal. Perhaps there is a topic that your class is studying about which you would like more information.

After you choose your topic, write two questions you have about it. Then do research to find the answers. Take notes on the facts you find.

My Topic: _____

Question 1: _____

Question 2: _____

My Notes: _____

_____

_____

_____

_____

_____

_____

_____

_____

RETURN Now go back to Al's work on page II3 in the Student Edition.

Prewriting

Organize

Use my notes to make a network tree.

The writer knew she had to organize her notes about meteors. Look at her network tree below to see how she organized them. This will help her when it is time to write the paragraphs of her first draft.

Topic
Meteors

Question 1
What are meteors?

Question 2
Do meteors ever land on Earth?

Fact
once thought to come from weather changes

Fact
chunks of rock and metal that usually come from comets

Fact
usually small and don't hit Earth

Fact
larger meteors that hit Earth called meteorites

Fact
called meteors when they come into Earth's atmosphere

Fact
called meteoroids when they go around the sun

Fact
can make craters

Fact
thousands of small meteorites found in Antarctica

Fact
pulled toward Earth by gravity

PrewRitiNg

Organize Use my notes to make a network tree.

your own writing

Now it's time for you to practice this strategy. Look back at what you wrote on page 65 of this book. Then fill in the network tree. You may need to add more bubbles to your network tree if you have found more than three facts for each of your questions.

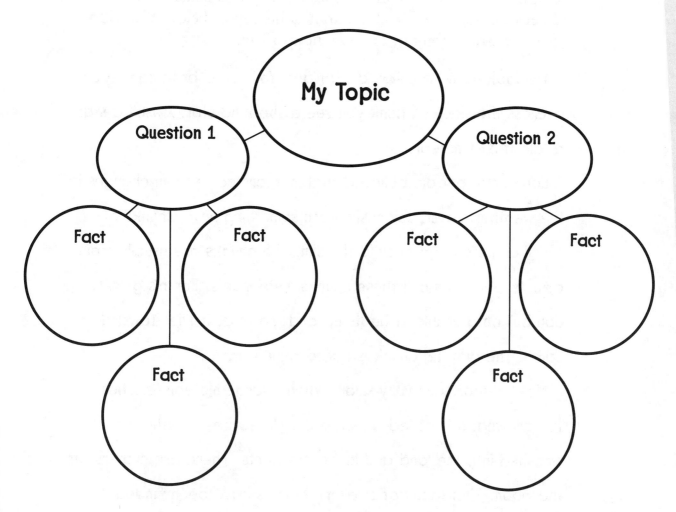

My Topic

Question 1   Question 2

Fact   Fact   Fact   Fact

Fact   Fact

RETURN

Now go back to Al's work on page 114 in the Student Edition.

Drafting

Write

Write an introduction that states the topic in an interesting way. Write one paragraph for every question on the network tree in the body. Write a conclusion to tie ideas together.

The writer wrote an interesting introduction that told the topic of the report. Her body paragraphs supported her topic and each paragraph answered one of the questions. Her conclusion tied all of her ideas together. Read the draft of her report below. You will see some errors. You can fix those now or later.

You look up on a clear, dark night. You see a brite light zoom accross the sky. you think you see a shooting star. It isn't a star at all. It is a meteor!

Long ago, people believed that meteors came from changes in the weather. Later, scientists learn something new. Chunks of metal and stone go around the sun. The chunks are usually from comets. Scientists call these chunks meteoroids. Earth's gravity can pull on a chunk. It heats up and glows as it flies toward Earth. The glowing chunk is called a meteor.

Most meteors are very small. When a large meteor reaches the grownd, it is called a meteorite. Meteorites sometimes smashed into the land and leave big dents. There are craters on the moon. Thousands of small meteorites have been finded in Antarctica Scientists also study the moon and planets like Jupiter.

A meteorite wont land in your living room. However, if you wait, you may see many meteors flash across the night sky!

Drafting

Write

Write an introduction that states the topic in an interesting way. Write one paragraph for every question on the network tree in the body. Write a conclusion to tie ideas together.

your own writing

Now it's time for you to practice this strategy. Draft your essay below using your network tree on page 67 to help you. Be sure to state the topic of your report in the first paragraph. Develop each body paragraph with its own main idea. Tie up your report and restate the topic in your conclusion. Continue your draft on the next page.

Introduction:

_____

_____

_____

_____

Body Paragraph:

_____

_____

_____

_____

_____

_____

_____

_____

_____

Drafting

Write

Write an introduction that states the topic in an interesting way. Write one paragraph for every question on the network tree in the body. Write a conclusion to tie ideas together.

Body Paragraph: _____

_____

_____

_____

_____

_____

_____

Conclusion: _____

_____

_____

_____

_____

_____

 Now go back to Al's work on page 116 in the Student Edition.

ReVising

Elaborate

Check that there is enough information in each body paragraph.

Now it's time for you to practice this strategy. The writer of the factual report on meteors decided to add important information. Here is the new information.

• The big dents are called craters.

• Scientists are still studying this huge supply of meteorites.

• Small meteors usually burn up before they hit Earth.

Read this paragraph from part of the writer's draft. Find a good place to add each sentence. Use a caret (∧) to show where each sentence should go. Then write the sentence. You will see some errors. You can fix those now or later.

Most meteors are very small. When a large meteor reaches the

grownd, it is called a meteorite. Meteorites sometimes smashed into

the land and leave big dents. There are craters on the moon.

Thousands of small meteorites have been finded in Antarctica

Remember: Use this strategy in *your own writing*

Now go back to Al's work on page 117 in the Student Edition.

Expository Writing • Factual Report

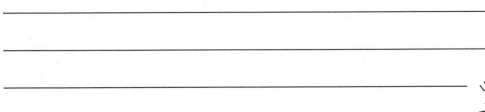

ReVising

Clarify

Check that all the facts have something to do with the topic of the report.

Now it's time for you to practice this strategy. The writer read her essay again. She remembered that all of the facts in her essay should clearly support her topic. When she read her essay again, she found sentences that do not support her topic. Read part of her essay below. Decide which two sentences do not support her topic. Cross out these sentences.

Most meteors are very small. Small meteors usually burn up

before they hit Earth. When a large meteor reaches the grownd,

it is called a meteorite. Meteorites sometimes smashed into the

land and leave big dents. The big dents are called craters.

There are craters on the moon. Thousands of small meteorites

have been finded in Antarctica Scientists are still studying this

huge supply of meteorites. Scientists also study the moon and

planets like Jupiter.

On the lines below, write why you decided these two sentences do not belong in the report on meteors.

_____

_____

_____

_____

Remember: Use this strategy in **your own writing**

 Now go back to Al's work on page 118 in the Student Edition.

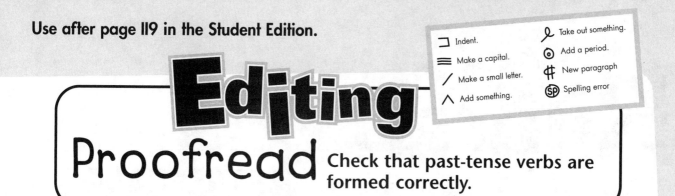

⅂ Indent.	ℓ Take out something.
≡ Make a capital.	⊙ Add a period.
/ Make a small letter.	⌗ New paragraph
∧ Add something.	ⓈⓅ Spelling error

Now it's time for you to practice this strategy. Here is a revised draft of the writer's factual report on meteors. You should always look for errors in spelling, grammar, and punctuation. Also look carefully to see that the correct form of past-tense verbs has been used. Use the proofreading marks to correct the errors. Use a dictionary to help with spelling.

You look up on a clear, dark night. You see a brite light zoom accross the sky. you think you see a shooting star. It isn't a star at all. It is a meteor!

Long ago, people believed that meteors came from changes in the weather. Later, scientists learn something new. Chunks of metal and stone go around the sun. The chunks are usually from comets. Scientists call these chunks meteoroids. Earth's gravity can pull on a chunk. It heats up and glows as it flies toward Earth. The glowing chunk is called a meteor.

Most meteors are very small. Small meteors usually burn up before they hit Earth. When a large meteor reaches the grownd, it is called a meteorite. Meteorites sometimes smashed into the land and leave big dents. The big dents are called craters. Thousands of small meteorites have been finded in Antarctica Scientists are still studying this huge supply of meteorites.

A meteorite won t land in your living room. However, if you wait, you may see many meteors flash across the night sky!

Remember: Use this strategy in **your own writing**

 Now go back to Al's work on page 120 in the Student Edition.

Using a Rubric

Use this rubric to assess Al's factual report on page 121 in your Student Edition. You may work with a partner.

Does an interesting introduction make the reader want to read more?

Is the report organized into an introduction, body, and conclusion?

Is there enough information in each body paragraph to support the main idea of the paragraph?

Do all of the facts have something to do with the topic of the report?

Are past-tense verbs formed correctly?

your own writing

Save this rubric. Use it to check your own writing.

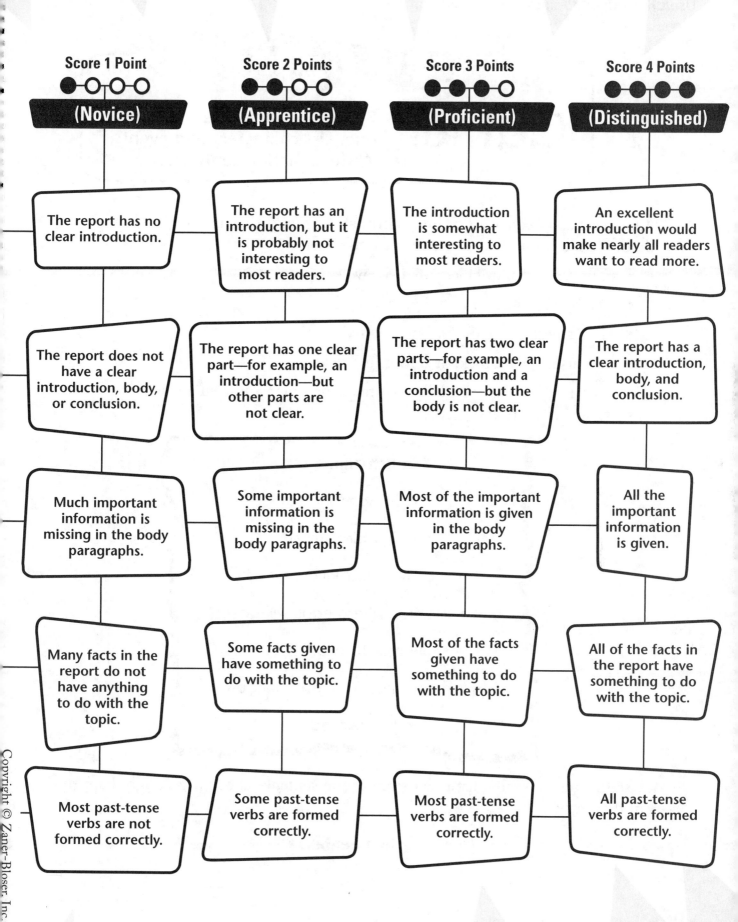

Score 1 Point (Novice)

The report has no clear introduction.

The report does not have a clear introduction, body, or conclusion.

Much important information is missing in the body paragraphs.

Many facts in the report do not have anything to do with the topic.

Most past-tense verbs are not formed correctly.

Score 2 Points (Apprentice)

The report has an introduction, but it is probably not interesting to most readers.

The report has one clear part—for example, an introduction—but other parts are not clear.

Some important information is missing in the body paragraphs.

Some facts given have something to do with the topic.

Some past-tense verbs are formed correctly.

Score 3 Points (Proficient)

The introduction is somewhat interesting to most readers.

The report has two clear parts—for example, an introduction and a conclusion—but the body is not clear.

Most of the important information is given in the body paragraphs.

Most of the facts given have something to do with the topic.

Most past-tense verbs are formed correctly.

Score 4 Points (Distinguished)

An excellent introduction would make nearly all readers want to read more.

The report has a clear introduction, body, and conclusion.

All the important information is given.

All of the facts in the report have something to do with the topic.

All past-tense verbs are formed correctly.

Prewriting

Gather

Brainstorm story ideas. Choose one. List characters and events. Write an action sentence.

One teacher asked a class to brainstorm about things they might find. Here is a list of what the class came up with:

- an unusual coin or object on a sidewalk
- a funny hat, shoe, or costume in school
- a bird's nest
- an unusual plant, rock, or flower in a field

One writer in the class decided to write about a bird's nest. Here is his list of characters and events.

Brainstorming List

- Otis and Nicole
- find bird's nest
- wonder what kind of bird
- question where eggs will go
- show nest to brother John
- see new nest from attic window
- put nest back

Use the brainstorming list to write an action sentence about what might happen in this story.

Action Sentence

_____ found _____

and they _____.

Narrative Writing • Realistic Story

Prewriting

Gather

Brainstorm story ideas. Choose one. List characters and events. Write an action sentence.

your own writing

Now it's your turn to practice this strategy with different topics. Think of something else that a character in a realistic story might find, or choose something else from the list on page 76.

Use the topic to think of what will happen in a story of your own. Choose names for your characters. What events would happen in your story?

My List

Characters:

Events:

Next, write an action sentence to tell what will happen in the story. Use the information you wrote above.

My Action Sentence

Who:

Does what:

How it comes out:

RETURN

Now go back to Lauren's work on page 136 in the Student Edition.

Prewriting

Organize

Make a storyboard. Write a caption for every picture.

Use the notes about Otis and Nicole on page 76 to draw three events in the order they might happen. The storyboard will help you organize events. You can make up some details if you want. Write a caption for each event.

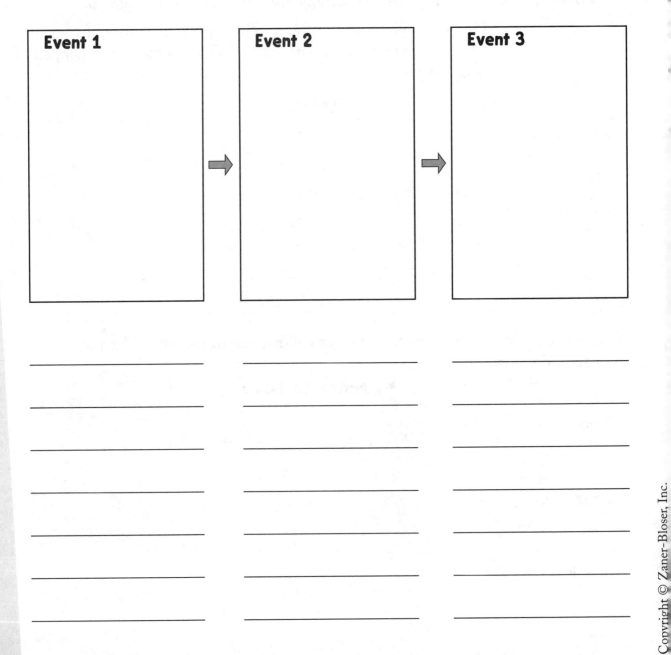

| Event 1 | Event 2 | Event 3 |

_____   _____   _____

_____   _____   _____

_____   _____   _____

_____   _____   _____

_____   _____   _____

Narrative Writing • *Realistic Story*

PrewRitiNg

Organize
Make a storyboard. Write a caption for every picture.

your own writing

Now it's time for you to practice this strategy. Use the notes you made about your topic from page 77 to draw three events from your own story. The storyboard will help you organize your events. Write captions for each of your events.

Event 1	Event 2	Event 3

_____ _____ _____

_____ _____ _____

_____ _____ _____

_____ _____ _____

_____ _____ _____

RETURN Now go back to Lauren's work on page 138 in the Student Edition.

Narrative Writing • Realistic Story

Drafting

Write
Draft my story. Make sure that my story has a clear beginning, middle, and end.

Read how one writer used the storyboard and captions from page 78 to write the beginning, middle, and end of a story.

Beginning	One Saturday morning, Nicole and Otis were playing football. As Otis ran to catch a pass, he suddenly stopped short. There in the grass not far from a maple tree was a bird's nest.

Middle	They showed the nest to their brother, John. He said it was a robin's nest. He helped them put the nest back in the maple tree.

End	The robin did not return to the nest that Nicole and Otis put in the tree. Then one day from their attic window, Nicole and Otis saw a new nest that the robin had built.

Drafting

Write

Draft my story. Make sure that my story has a clear beginning, middle, and end.

your own writing

Now it's time for you to practice this strategy. Use your own storyboard and captions from page 79 to write the beginning, middle, and end of your own story.

Beginning

Middle

End

RETURN
Now go back to Lauren's work on page 140 in the Student Edition.

ReVising

Elaborate
Add dialogue to make my characters seem more real.

Read the following dialogue sentences. Pay special attention to all the punctuation.

Sentence A. "Maybe it fell out of the tree," she said.

Sentence B. "Don't we have a catcher's mask in the attic?" Otis asked.

Sentence C. They both shouted, "Look at what we found!"

Sentence D. "See the grass and twigs? See the mud that holds them together?"

Now rewrite each sentence below as a dialogue sentence. Name a speaker for sentences 1., 2., and 3. Don't forget the quotation marks and the rest of the punctuation.

Use Sentences A, B, C, and D to help you with all the punctuation.

1. It's a robin's nest. (Use sentence A as a guide to punctuation.)

_____

_____

2. Should we put the nest back in the tree? (Use sentence B as a guide to punctuation.)

_____

_____

3. The robin will come back to lay her eggs. (Use sentence C as a guide to punctuation.)

_____

_____

4. Let's check the nest every day for the eggs. (Use sentence D as a guide to punctuation.)

_____

_____

Narrative Writing • Realistic Story

Revising

Elaborate

Add dialogue to make my characters seem more real.

Now it's time for you to practice this strategy. Read part of one writer's story about finding a robin's nest. Where could you add the dialogue? Add **any** of the dialogue sentences from page 82 to this part of the story. You should add at least two dialogue sentences.

Nicole hurried over to look at the nest. She and Otis were excited.

Nicole picked up the nest very carefully. She wanted to show it

---

to John, their oldest brother.

Otis ran into the house. Nicole followed more slowly with the nest.

John looked at the nest.

Remember: Use this strategy in **your own writing**

 Now go back to Lauren's work on page 141 in the Student Edition.

ReVising

Clarify

Reorder sentences to make sure the story flows well and makes sense.

Now it's time for you to practice this strategy. Read these two paragraphs from one writer's story about the bird's nest. How can you move the sentences so that the order makes sense? Rewrite the paragraphs with the sentences in a better order.

After they put the nest back, hours passed. The week passed.

Days passed. Otis and Nicole did not see any robins near the branches

that held the nest. "Poor robin has no nest," they said.

"Don't we have a catcher's mask in the attic?" Otis asked. The

next Saturday morning Nicole and Otis were tossing a softball.

"Let's get the mask."

_____

_____

_____

_____

_____

_____

Remember:
Use this strategy in
your own writing

 RETURN Now go back to Lauren's work on page 142 in the Student Edition.

Editing

Proofread

Check to see that all pronouns are in their correct form.

Now it's time for you to practice this strategy. Here is part of one writer's realistic story about the robin's nest. Use the proofreading marks to correct the errors. Use a dictionary to help with spelling.

Otis ran into the house. Nicole followed more slowly with the nest. Them both shouted, "Look what we found!"

John looked at the nest. "It's a robin's nest," he said. "See the grass and twigs? See the mud that holds them together? Let's put the nest back into the tree. Maybe the robin will come back to lay her eggs."

That is what them did John lifted up Otis and Otis carefully tucked the nest between too branches of the leafy maple tree.

After they put the nest back, hours passed. Days passed. The week passed. Otis and Nicole did not see any robins near the branches that held the nest. "Poor robin has no nest," they said.

The next Saturday morning Nicole and Otis were tossing a softball. "Don't we have a catcher's mask in the attic?" Otis asked. "Let's get the mask." Him and Nicole ran into the house and up the stairs to the attic. As they looked for the mask, Nicole glanced owt the tiny attic window.

"Otis, look!" she shouted.

A new robin's nest sat almost at the top of the maple tree. Inside were three bright blue eggs.

Remember: Use this strategy in **your own writing**

 RETURN Now go back to Lauren's work on page 144 in the Student Edition.

Using a Rubric

Use this rubric to check Lauren's realistic story on pages 145–147 in your Student Edition. You may work with a partner.

Audience

Does the writer choose a topic that is interesting to the readers?

Organization

Is the story easy to follow with a clear beginning, middle, and end?

Elaboration

Does the story have dialogue to make the characters seem more real?

Clarification

Does each sentence lead clearly to the next sentence?

Conventions & Skills

Are all pronouns in their correct form?

your own writing

Save this rubric. Use it to check your own writing.

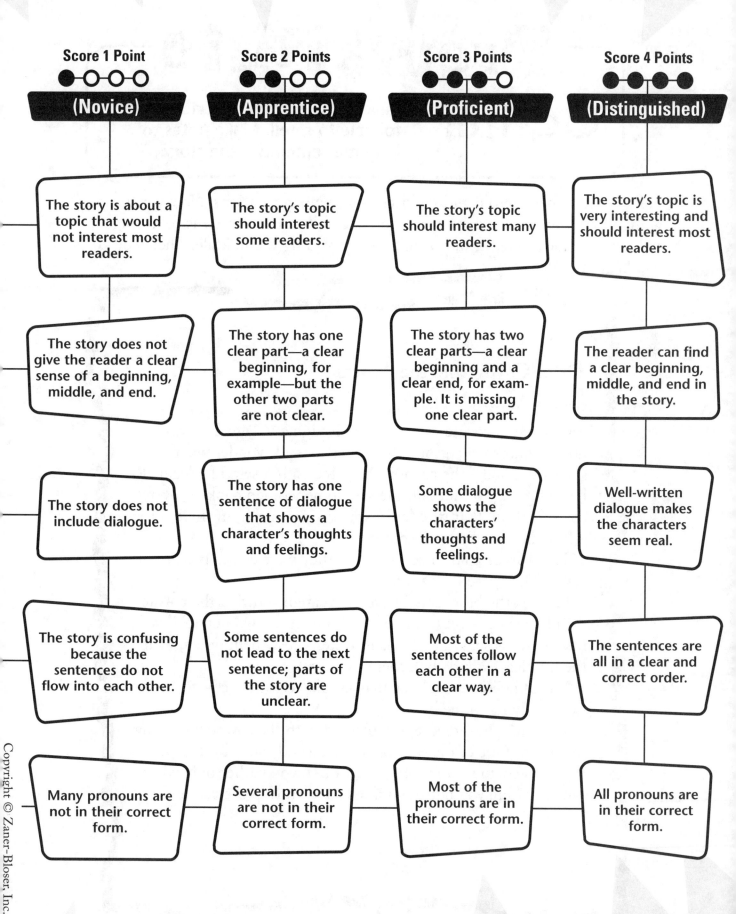

Score 1 Point (Novice)

The story is about a topic that would not interest most readers.

The story does not give the reader a clear sense of a beginning, middle, and end.

The story does not include dialogue.

The story is confusing because the sentences do not flow into each other.

Many pronouns are not in their correct form.

Score 2 Points (Apprentice)

The story's topic should interest some readers.

The story has one clear part—a clear beginning, for example—but the other two parts are not clear.

The story has one sentence of dialogue that shows a character's thoughts and feelings.

Some sentences do not lead to the next sentence; parts of the story are unclear.

Several pronouns are not in their correct form.

Score 3 Points (Proficient)

The story's topic should interest many readers.

The story has two clear parts—a clear beginning and a clear end, for example. It is missing one clear part.

Some dialogue shows the characters' thoughts and feelings.

Most of the sentences follow each other in a clear way.

Most of the pronouns are in their correct form.

Score 4 Points (Distinguished)

The story's topic is very interesting and should interest most readers.

The reader can find a clear beginning, middle, and end in the story.

Well-written dialogue makes the characters seem real.

The sentences are all in a clear and correct order.

All pronouns are in their correct form.

Prewriting

Gather

Read some folktales. Decide which folktale to retell. Make notes to help me remember the story.

Folktales have been retold and rewritten for many generations. Now you are going to rewrite one of your favorite folktales. You can choose the following folktale, or choose one of your own. Start by reading the folktale. Then, you will begin to retell it by rewriting it.

Title: Coyote and the Acorns

(Native American folktale)

One day, a coyote was passing through a village. He was hungry and smelled something delicious. "I wonder what smells so good?" the coyote whispered to himself. He decided he was going to find out. He saw some women cooking over coals. "I think that wonderful smell is coming from there. I'll ask them what they are cooking."

The women told the coyote that they were cooking acorn cakes. They gave him a bite to try.

"This is the best food I have ever eaten!" howled the coyote.

"The recipe is very simple," said one of the women. "All you have to do is soak the acorns in water, press them down, wrap them in leaves, and cook them over coals."

"I can't believe it could be that simple," cried the coyote. "You must be lying to me."

The women were not very pleased with the coyote for calling them liars. One of the women spoke up and said, "I'll tell you the real way to make acorn cakes. First, you gather only white acorns. Then, you put them in a canoe and tip the canoe over

Narrative Writing • Folktale

Prewriting

Gather

Read some folktales. Decide which folktale to retell. Make notes to help me remember the story.

in the middle of the river. Find all the acorns and grind them using flat stones. Cook them over firewood that has been taken from the top of a tree. Don't forget to peel off all the bark. Then you must wrap the acorn mixture in poison ivy leaves."

The coyote didn't even bother to say thank you before he was off in search of white acorns. He set out to do exactly what the woman told him to do. He gathered the acorns, tipped them in the river, and gathered the poison ivy leaves. The poison ivy leaves made him scream with pain as he touched them. He was still determined. When it came time to get the acorns from the bottom of the river, he could not find them. The coyote knew he must have done something wrong. Sadly, he walked back to the village. On the way, he saw a stranger. He asked the stranger if he knew how to make acorn cakes.

"Sure," said the stranger. "All you have to do is soak the acorns in water, press them down, wrap them in leaves, and cook them over coals."

"Oh, oh, oh!" cried the coyote. "I have learned my lesson the hard way."

Prewriting

Gather

Read some folktales. Decide which folktale to retell. Make notes to help me remember the story.

your own writing

Now it's time for you to practice this strategy. Use this page to make notes on your folktale. You can retell "Coyote and the Acorns" or the folktale that you chose. Include the main characters, the problem, and the events. You can also use this space to brainstorm ways to make small changes in the folktale.

Name of folktale:

Main characters:

Problem:

Notes:

Now go back to Lu-yin's work on page 160 in the Student Edition.

Narrative Writing • Folktale

Prewriting

Organize
Use my notes to make a story map.

your own writing

Now it's time for you to practice this strategy. Use the story map on this page to organize your notes from page 90. Write how you will introduce the problem in the Beginning box. Write the events of the story in the Middle box. Write how the story came out in the end in the End box.

Beginning

Middle

End

RETURN Now go back to Lu-yin's work on page 162 in the Student Edition.

Drafting

Write

Set up the folktale by telling the main characters, setting, and problem in the first paragraph.

your own writing

Now it's time for you to practice this strategy. Use the space on this page and the next page to draft your folktale. Remember to include the important information in your first paragraph. Be sure to tell the main character or characters, the setting, and some idea of what the problem is going to be. You can use your story map from page 91 to help you. Also you can add details of your own to make the folktale more interesting.

_____

_____

_____

_____

_____

_____

_____

_____

_____

Drafting

Write

Set up the folktale by telling the main characters, setting, and problem in the first paragraph.

Continue writing your folktale on this page.

_____

_____

_____

_____

_____

_____

_____

_____

_____

_____

 Now go back to Lu-yin's work on page 164 in the Student Edition.

ReVising

Elaborate
Add exact words to make the story more interesting.

Now it's your turn to practice this strategy. Here are some paragraphs from one writer's draft of the retelling of "Coyote and the Acorns."

Read the draft. Pay special attention to the underlined words. Choose an exact word from the box to replace each underlined word. Cross out the words you want to replace. Write each exact word above each word you cross out. You may see mistakes in the draft. You can fix mistakes now or later.

Exact Words

acorn cakes	growled	answered
soak	asked	wrap

Coyote <u>said</u>, "How do you make such wonderful <u>things</u>?"

The woman <u>said</u>, "Its easy. You gather acorns. You <u>put</u> them in water and press them down hard for two days. Then you <u>put</u> leaves around them and cook them over hot coals." She was weaving a beautiful blanket for her grandson.

"Nonsense!" <u>said</u> Coyote "That's too easy for something this good." Coyote didn't have any children. Then he growled, "You must be lying."

Remember:
Use this strategy in
**your own
writing**

Now go back to Lu-yin's work on page 165 in the Student Edition.

ReVising

Clarify

Take out information that doesn't help tell my story.

Now it's time for you to practice this strategy. The writer remembered that the rubric said to include details and events that help tell the story. Read through this part of the writer's draft and draw a line through any sentence that doesn't help tell the story. You will see some mistakes as you read. You can fix them now or later.

One summer day long ago, a coyote was walking through a village deep in a forest. He had been there many times before. Suddenly, he smelled something delicious. he wanted some of whatever it was. Then he saw women cooking. "I want some of that, and I want the recipe, too," he said softly to himself. This should not have been a problem, but Coyote did not trust people to tell him the truth.

"Whut is that wonderful smell?" asked Coyote. "It is the deliciousest smell."

"You smell acorn cakes," a woman answered. "Would you like some"

Coyote nodded. He ate the first cake. Then he ate another and another and another. Finally, when every cake was gone, he said, "These are the wonderfulest acorn cakes I have ever eaten!" Coyote thought they were even better than the stew he had eaten for breakfast! Coyote

ReVising

Clarify

Take out information that doesn't help tell my story.

asked, "How do you make such wonderful acorn cakes?"

The woman answered, "Its easy. You gather acorns. You soak them in water and press them down hard for two days. Then you wrap leaves around them and cook them over hot coals." She was weaving a beautiful blanket for her grandson.

"Nonsense!" growled Coyote "That's too easy for something this good." Coyote didn't have any children. Then he growled, "You must be lying."

On the following lines, write one of the sentences you crossed out. Then write why you took it out.

_____

_____

_____

_____

Remember: Use this strategy in *your own writing*

 Now go back to Lu-yin's work on page 166 in the Student Edition.

Narrative Writing • Folktale

Editing

Proofread

Check that the correct form is used when an adjective compares two or more things.

Now it's your turn to practice this strategy. Here is one writer's revised draft of the folktale about Coyote and acorn cakes. Use the proofreading marks to correct the errors. Use a dictionary to help with spelling.

Coyote Learns a Lesson

One summer day long ago, a coyote was walking through a village deep in a forest. Suddenly, he smelled something delicious. he wanted some of whatever it was. Then he saw women cooking. "I want some of that, and I want the recipe, too," he said softly to himself. This should not have been a problem, but Coyote did not trust people to tell him the truth.

"Whut is that wonderful smell?" asked Coyote. "It is the deliciousest smell."

"You smell acorn cakes," a woman answered. "Would you like some "

Coyote nodded. He ate the first cake. Then he ate another and another and another. Finally, when every cake was gone, he said, "These are the wonderfulest

Editing

Proofread

Check that the correct form is used when an adjective compares two or more things.

acorn cakes I have ever eaten!" Coyote asked, "How do you make such wonderful acorn cakes?"

The woman answered, "It s easy. You gather acorns. You soak them in water and press them down hard for two days. Then you wrap leaves around them and cook them over hot coals."

"Nonsense!" growled Coyote "That's too easy for something this good." Then he growled, "You must be lying."

The woman thought fast and replied, "You are rite, Coyote. I'll tell you the real way to make the cakes."

She said, "First, gather only the most tiniest white acorns. Put them in a canoe. Then tip the canoe over in the middle of a river. Find all the acorns, and grind them with two flat stones. For firewood, use only wood from the top of a tree, but be sure to peel off all the bark first. Last, wrap the acorns in poison ivy leaves."

Without saying a word of thanks, Coyote got started He gather only tiny white acorns, which took him two days. He put the acorns in a canoe in a raging river and tipped

┐ Indent.　　　　　　ℓ Take out something.

≡ Make a capital.　　◉ Add a period.

∕ Make a small letter.　⌗ New paragraph

∧ Add something.　　㏚ Spelling error

Editing

Proofread

Check that the correct form is used when an adjective compares two or more things.

the canoe over. Then he looked for flat stones. The stones were even more hard to find than the acorns. He got wood from the most tall tree, but it took him three days to peal all the bark. When he gathered the poison ivy leaves, the poison stung his paws. That made him howl in pain. Then he tried to get his acorns from the bottom of the river. He dove and dove and dove but he could not find any of them.

Feeling sad, coyote went back to the village. He wanted to know what he had done wrong. He ask a stranger, "How do you make acorn cakes?"

The stranger said "You gather acorns. You soak them in water and press them down hard for two days. Then you wrap leaves around them and cook them over hot coals."

"Oh! Oh! Oh!" howled Coyote. Coyote had learned his lesson, but he had learned it the hard way.

Remember:
Use this strategy in
your own
writing

RETURN Now go back to Lu-yin's work on page 168 in the Student Edition.

Using a Rubric

Use this rubric to check Lu-yin's retold folktale on pages 169–171 in your Student Edition. You may work with a partner.

Audience

Does the writer get the reader interested in the story by telling the main characters, the setting, and the problem in the first paragraph?

Organization

Does the story have a clear beginning, middle, and end?

Elaboration

Does the writer use exact words to make the story more interesting?

Clarification

Do all of the details and events help tell the story?

Conventions & Skills

Is the correct form used when an adjective compares two or more things?

your own writing

Save this rubric. Use it to check your own writing.

Score 1 Point	Score 2 Points	Score 3 Points	Score 4 Points
●○○○	●●○○	●●●○	●●●●
(Novice)	**(Apprentice)**	**(Proficient)**	**(Distinguished)**
The writer gives the reader little information in the first paragraph.	The writer interests the reader by giving some of the information needed in the first paragraph.	The writer interests the reader by giving most of the information needed in the first paragraph.	The writer gives all the needed information in the first paragraph in an interesting way.
The story does not have a clear beginning, middle, and end.	The story has one clear part—a clear beginning, for example—but the other parts are not clear.	The story has two clear parts—a clear beginning and a clear end, for example.	The story has a clear beginning, middle, and end.
The writer uses few exact words.	The writer uses some exact words.	Many exact words are used.	The writer always uses exact words.
There are many unrelated details that do not help tell the story.	There are some unrelated details that do not help tell the story.	Most of the details and events help tell the story.	All of the details and events help tell the story.
Adjectives that compare are almost never in the correct form.	There are some errors in the form of adjectives that compare two or more things.	Most adjectives that compare are correct.	The writer always uses the correct form of adjectives that compare two or more things.

Prewriting

Gather

Use interviews to gather information. Take notes and put the answers you get to each question together.

Many students have strong feelings about riding the bus to school every day. Some of them enjoy the ride, and some don't. Read the following interview questions and answers one writer received. The answers to these questions will be helpful to the writer in organizing and writing a persuasive paragraph.

Topic: Riding the School Bus

Interview Questions and Answers:

1. **Question:** How long does the bus ride take for you?

   Answer: It takes a long time. It is too long.

2. **Question:** What do you think of the seats on the bus?

   Answer: The seats on the bus are bumpy and hard.

3. **Question:** What do you like or dislike about riding the school bus?

   Answer: I don't like the school bus because the ride is uncomfortable.

4. **Question:** What do you think of the rules for riding on the bus?

   Answer: The rules for riding the school bus are too strict.

Prewriting

Gather

Use interviews to gather information. Take notes and put the answers you get to each question together.

your own writing

Now it's your turn to practice this strategy with a different topic. Pick a topic about which you have an opinion. Some topics might be: food in the cafeteria, your favorite subject, or which animal makes the best pet. Begin gathering information about your topic by interviewing one or more of your classmates. Write out your questions and take notes during the interviews.

Topic:
_____

Interview Questions and Answers:
_____

_____

_____

_____

_____

_____

_____

_____

_____

_____

_____

_____

 RETURN Now go back to Louis's work on page 185 in the Student Edition.

Prewriting

Organize

Use my notes to make a main-idea table.

The student writer decided on the following main idea (the student's opinion):

Riding the school bus is not a pleasant way to start the day.

The writer organized the answers he received from his interviews into the main-idea table below. The answers to the questions are the reasons that support his opinion. They will become the detail sentences in his persuasive paragraph. Read how he organized the answers below.

Main Idea (Student's Opinion):
Riding the school bus is not a pleasant way to start the day.

Supporting Detail (a reason)	Supporting Detail (a reason)	Supporting Detail (a reason)	Supporting Detail (a reason)
The ride takes too long.	The ride is uncomfortable.	The ride is too bumpy.	There are too many rules for riding the bus.

Prewriting

Organize
Use my notes to make a main-idea table.

your own writing

Now it's time for you to practice this strategy. Organize the answers you received from your interviews on your topic into the following main-idea table.

Main Idea (Student's Opinion):
_____

Supporting Detail (a reason)	Supporting Detail (a reason)	Supporting Detail (a reason)	Supporting Detail (a reason)
_____	_____	_____	_____
_____	_____	_____	_____
_____	_____	_____	_____
_____	_____	_____	_____
_____	_____	_____	_____
_____	_____	_____	_____
_____	_____	_____	_____
_____	_____	_____	_____

RETURN

Now go back to Louis's work on page 186 in the Student Edition.

Drafting

Write
State my opinion in the first sentence. Support my opinion in the middle of the paragraph. Restate my opinion in the last sentence.

Not everyone dislikes riding a school bus. A different student writer decided that riding the school bus *is* a very pleasant way to start the day. Here is the first sentence of her persuasive paragraph.

Riding the school bus is a very pleasant way to start the day.

Below and on the next page are ten sentences. Some of them give reasons to support this writer's opinion. Some of them restate this writer's opinion and could be used as the last sentence in her paragraph.

After each sentence, write **Reason** if the sentence gives a reason for the opinion. Write **Restatement** if the sentence repeats the opinion.

1. I enjoy seeing my friends on the bus every morning. _____

2. It's fun to sit with Lee, who is a special friend of mine. _____

3. Remember, riding the school bus every morning can start your day right! _____

4. I like to look out the window and see my friends standing on the corner waiting for the bus. _____

5. Mrs. Cormier, the bus driver, always wishes me a good morning when I get on the bus. _____

6. Nothing starts my day better than a pleasant ride on the school bus. _____

Drafting

Write

State my opinion in the first sentence. Support my opinion in the middle of the paragraph. Restate my opinion in the last sentence.

7. The seats are comfortable, and the ride is smooth. _____

8. Sometimes we sing or tell jokes on the bus. _____

9. I can talk with my friends about the book we're reading or about our homework. _____

10. If you are like me, you enjoy riding the bus to school every morning. _____

11. I look over my homework on the bus, so I have another chance to make sure it is right. _____

12. I can think about what I'm going to do when I get to school. _____

Complete the Drafting activity on the next page.

Drafting

Write

State my opinion in the first sentence. Support my opinion in the middle of the paragraph. Restate my opinion in the last sentence.

your own writing

Now it's time for you to practice this strategy. Look back at the notes you made on page 103 of this book. Look at the reasons you came up with to support your opinion on page 105 of this book. Use this information to begin drafting your own persuasive paragraph below.

_____

_____

_____

_____

_____

_____

_____

_____

_____

_____

_____

_____

Now go back to Louis's work on page 188 in the Student Edition.

Persuasive Writing • Persuasive Paragraph

Revising

Elaborate
Add signal words that make my paragraph easy to understand.

Now it's time for you to practice this strategy. Here are some sentences from students who either like or don't like riding the school bus. Fill in the sentences with signal words from the box. There is more than one right answer for some of the sentences, but use each answer only once.

Signal Words

therefore	as a result	for this reason
because	the reason why	

1. Students should ride the school bus _____ going in separate cars wastes energy.

2. We sing and tell jokes on the bus.

   _____, I am always in a good mood when I get to school.

3. I can talk with my friends about schoolwork.

   _____, I can learn on the bus!

4. The seats on the school bus are not comfortable.

   _____, I do not enjoy riding on the bus.

5. I do not like to ride the school bus. _____ is that the bus driver is too strict.

Remember: Use this strategy in **your own writing**

RETURN Now go back to Louis's work on page 189 in the Student Edition.

ReVising

Clarify

Look for stringy sentences and separate them.

Now it's time for you to practice this strategy. The following sentences are from students who either like or dislike riding the school bus. Separate each stringy sentence. Write the new sentences on the lines below.

1. We sing songs on the bus, and sometimes we play twenty questions, and sometimes we watch for out-of-state license plates, and sometimes we tell jokes, so we always have fun.

_____

_____

_____

_____

2. Some seats are torn or lumpy, and the air inside the school bus is stuffy, and the ride is always bumpy, and I get bounced around.

_____

_____

_____

3. The bus drivers are strict, so no one can eat, drink, play music, or yell, and we never have any fun, and all we do is sit there.

_____

_____

Remember: Use this strategy in *your own writing*

RETURN Now go back to Louis's work on page 190 in the Student Edition.

Editing
Proofread
Check that all proper nouns have been capitalized.

Indent. / Make a capital. / Make a small letter. / Add something. / Take out something. / Add a period. / New paragraph / Spelling error

Now it's time for you to practice this strategy. Here is part of one writer's revised draft of a persuasive paragraph about riding the school bus. Use the proofreading marks to correct the errors. Use a dictionary to help with spelling.

The Trouble With Riding the School Bus

On monday, I got on the bus at 8:15. I did not get to oak street school until 8:55. Last week, when my dad brought me to school in his car, the trip took only 15 minutes. That means when I go by bus, I might spend almost an extra half hour to get to school. I talked to tommy about this problem. He said his ride was ten minutes by car and thirty minutes by bus.

The air inside the school bus is stuffy. Worst of all, the ride is allways bumpy. One last reason for not liking the bus ride is the rules. Our bus driver, Mrs. mifflin, is very nice, but the rules are very strict. No one can eat, drink, play music, or talk loudly. We can't have any fun. All we can do is sit there. That makes a long ride seem even longer.

Remember: Use this strategy in **your own writing**

 Now go back to Louis's work on page 192 in the Student Edition.

Persuasive Writing • Persuasive Paragraph

111

Using a Rubric

Use this rubric to assess Louis's persuasive paragraph on page 193 in your Student Edition. You may work with a partner.

Does the first sentence let the reader know the writer's opinion?

Do the middle sentences support the writer's opinion? Does the last sentence restate the opinion?

How well does the writer use signal words to make the paragraph easy to understand?

Has the writer avoided stringy sentences (sentences with too many *and*'s or *so*'s)?

Are all proper nouns capitalized?

★ your own writing ★

Save this rubric. Use it to check your own writing.

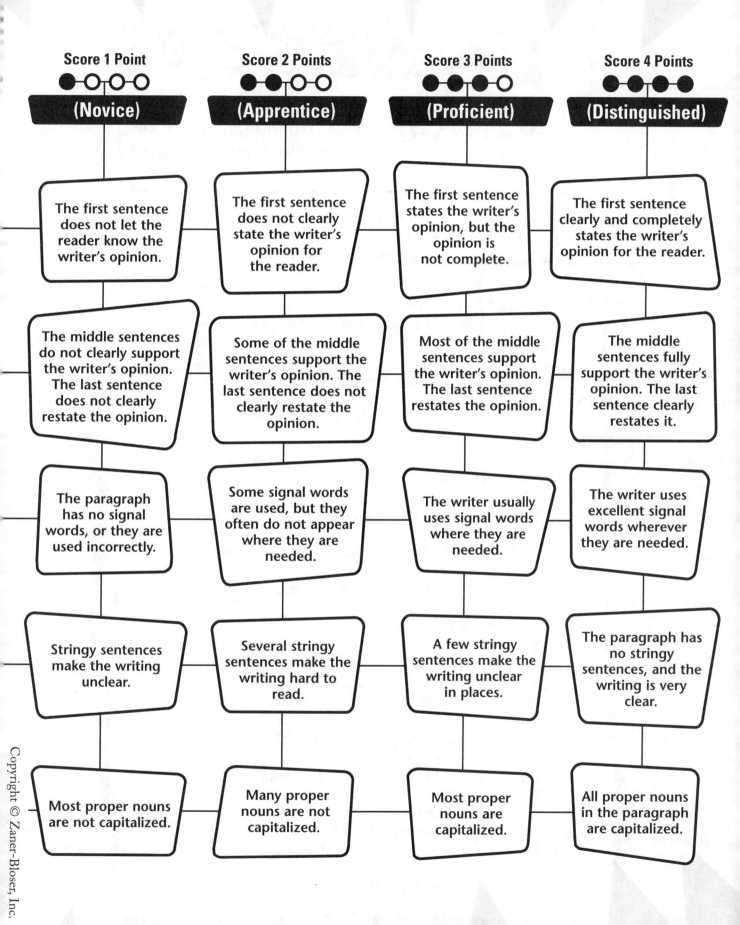

Score 1 Point (Novice)	Score 2 Points (Apprentice)	Score 3 Points (Proficient)	Score 4 Points (Distinguished)
The first sentence does not let the reader know the writer's opinion.	The first sentence does not clearly state the writer's opinion for the reader.	The first sentence states the writer's opinion, but the opinion is not complete.	The first sentence clearly and completely states the writer's opinion for the reader.
The middle sentences do not clearly support the writer's opinion. The last sentence does not clearly restate the opinion.	Some of the middle sentences support the writer's opinion. The last sentence does not clearly restate the opinion.	Most of the middle sentences support the writer's opinion. The last sentence restates the opinion.	The middle sentences fully support the writer's opinion. The last sentence clearly restates it.
The paragraph has no signal words, or they are used incorrectly.	Some signal words are used, but they often do not appear where they are needed.	The writer usually uses signal words where they are needed.	The writer uses excellent signal words wherever they are needed.
Stringy sentences make the writing unclear.	Several stringy sentences make the writing hard to read.	A few stringy sentences make the writing unclear in places.	The paragraph has no stringy sentences, and the writing is very clear.
Most proper nouns are not capitalized.	Many proper nouns are not capitalized.	Most proper nouns are capitalized.	All proper nouns in the paragraph are capitalized.

Copyright © Zaner-Bloser, Inc.

Prewriting

Gather

Choose a topic about which I have a strong opinion. Make notes on the reasons for my opinion.

Here is a school topic about which one writer has a strong opinion. This writer feels that the school cafeteria should serve pizza every day. Read the reasons she gathered below. What are the two big reasons she has for wanting the school cafeteria to serve pizza every day? Write Reason 1 beside one of the reasons and Reason 2 beside the other. All of the other reasons are smaller facts that support these two big reasons.

My Opinion: The school cafeteria should serve pizza every day.

My Reasons:

- can be very good for people

- one or more bread servings from crust

- always long lines to buy pizza

- vegetable serving from tomato sauce

- dairy serving from the cheese

- almost everyone likes pizza

- more popular than spaghetti or macaroni and cheese

- the most popular menu item in cafeteria

- cheese in pizza has calcium and protein

- more popular than hot dogs

- cafeteria sometimes runs out of pizza

- tomatoes in pizza have vitamin C and water

Prewriting

Gather
Choose a topic about which I have a strong opinion. Make notes on the reasons for my opinion.

your own writing

Now it's your turn to practice this strategy with another topic. Here are some school topics about which you might have a strong opinion.

- Our school should teach life saving, swimming, or something else.
- The school library should have videos, DVD players, or more computers hooked up to the Internet.
- Our school should raise money for an organization, a specific charity, something that students want to do, or something else.

Choose one or think of a topic of your own to write about. Fill in the blanks below to gather notes for your essay. First, write your opinion. Then write as many reasons as you can think of to back up your opinion.

My Opinion: _____

_____

My Reasons:

- _____

- _____

- _____

- _____

- _____

- _____

- _____

- _____

 Now go back to Luke's work on page 203 in the Student Edition.

PreWriting

Organize Use my notes to make a network tree.

Here is how the writer organized her notes about why her school should serve pizza more often in the cafeteria. Look to see how she used a network tree. Pay special attention to how she used her two big facts as Reason 1 and Reason 2. All of the smaller facts fit under these reasons.

My Opinion
The school cafeteria should serve pizza every day.

Reason 1
Pizza can be very good for people.

Reason 2
Almost everyone likes pizza.

Fact
Pizza gives you servings from vegetable, bread, and dairy food groups.

Fact
Cheese in pizza has calcium and protein.

Fact
Tomatoes in pizza have vitamin C and water.

Fact
It is more popular than spaghetti, macaroni and cheese, or hot dogs.

Fact
There are always long lines to buy pizza.

Fact
Cafeteria sometimes runs out of pizza.

Copyright © Zaner-Bloser, Inc.

PreWRitiNg

Organize
Use my notes to make a network tree.

your own writing

Now it's time for you to practice this strategy. Look back at the notes you made on page 115. If you have more than two reasons use another piece of paper so you can add more bubbles. Organize your notes into a network tree.

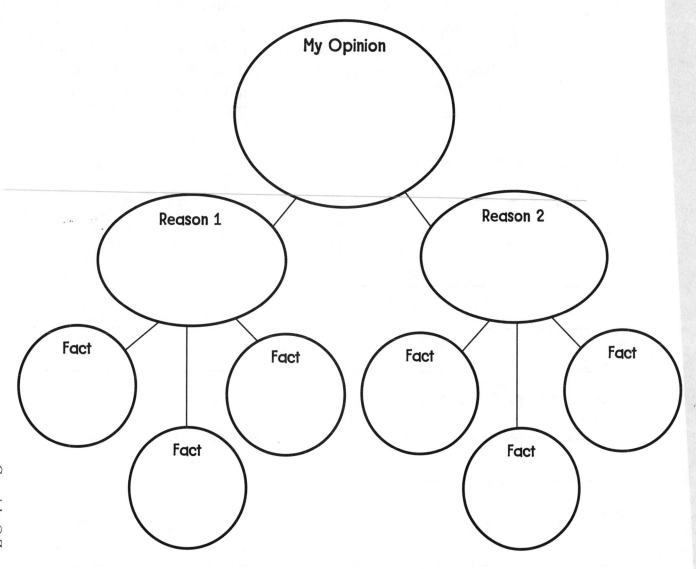

My Opinion

Reason 1

Reason 2

Fact

Fact

Fact

Fact

Fact

Fact

RETURN
Now go back to Luke's work on page 204 in the Student Edition.

Drafting

Write
Draft my essay. Write one paragraph for the introduction. Write one paragraph for the first reason and one paragraph for the second reason. Write one paragraph for the conclusion.

your own
writing

Now it's time for you to practice this strategy. Use the notes and the network tree you made to draft your essay below and on the next page. Don't forget to state your opinion in the first paragraph. Remember to support your opinion with reasons and facts in the body paragraphs. Finally, restate your opinion in your concluding paragraph. If you need more room use another sheet of paper.

Introduction (State opinion.)

_____

_____

_____

_____

_____

Body Paragraph (Reason 1)

_____

_____

_____

_____

_____

Drafting

Write
Draft my essay. Write one paragraph for the introduction. Write one paragraph for the first reason and one paragraph for the second reason. Write one paragraph for the conclusion.

Body Paragraph (Reason 2)

_____

_____

_____

_____

_____

_____

_____

Conclusion (Restate opinion.)

_____

_____

_____

_____

_____

_____

 Now go back to Luke's work on page 206 in the Student Edition.

Revising

Elaborate Add facts to back up my reasons.

Now it's time for you to practice this strategy. Read the paragraph at the bottom of the page. It gives the second reason why the writer feels the cafeteria should serve pizza every day. She wants to add more facts to back up the second reason. Here are some facts that could be added:

- Still, students buy pizza more often than they buy hot dogs.
- You see students throw away plates of macaroni and cheese.
- Some students even buy a second slice.

Add these facts in the correct place in the writer's paragraph below. Also, add any facts of your own.

Almost everyone eats pizza and the school should supply enough for everybody. Hot dogs is also popular. However, most people don't like the cafeteria spaghetti. Almost no one buys it. they do not like the cafeteria's macaroni and cheese either. Lots of students eat the cafeteria pizza, though. The lines are always long on pizza day. Students do not throw half their pizza away at the end of lunch. Sometimes the cafeteria even runs out of pizza on pizza day. Students really like pizza.

Remember: Use this strategy in **your own writing**

 RETURN Now go back to Luke's work on page 207 in the Student Edition.

ReVising

Clarify — Take out facts and details that do not support my opinion.

Now it's time for you to practice this strategy. Help the writer with the conclusion of the pizza essay. Cross out facts and details that do not support her opinion.

Pizza can be one part of a healthy diet Fruit is also part

of a healthy diet. it is also a food that people likes to eat.

People usually like chocolate, too. If our school cafeteria

served pizza every day, students might be healthier. They

certainly would be happier! Cookies would make students

even happier.

On the lines below, write why you decided to delete the facts and details that you did.

_____

_____

_____

_____

_____

Remember: Use this strategy in **your own writing**

 RETURN Now go back to Luke's work on page 208 in the Student Edition.

Proofread
Check that subjects and verbs always agree.

Now it's time for you to practice this strategy. Here is a revised draft of the persuasive essay about pizza. Use the proofreading marks to correct the errors. Look for errors in subject-verb agreement in addition to spelling, grammar, and punctuation errors. Use a dictionary to help with spelling.

Pizza Every Day

Pizza is good for you. It tastes great. Pizza is quick and easy to eat, too. It is the best thing our school cafeteria serves. On piza day, almost everyone buys lunch. Our school should serve pizza every day.

Pizza gives your body what it needs. It gives you servings from different food groups. Cheese belongs to the dairy group. Cheese has calcium. It help bones grow and stay strong. Cheese also has protein. We needs to eat protein every day. The pizza sauce are made from tomatoes. Tomatoes are in the vegetable food group. They have vitamin C and water. Pizza crust is in the bread food group

Editing

Proofread Check that subjects and verbs always agree.

Almost everyone eats pizza and the school should supply enough for everybody. Hot dogs is popular. Still, students buy pizza more often than they buy hot dogs. However, most people don't like the spaghetti. Almost no one buys it. they do not like the cafeteria's macaroni and cheese either. You see students throw away plates of macaroni and cheese. Lots of students eat the cafeteria pizza, though. The lines are always long on pizza day. Students do not throw half their pizza away at the end of lunch. Some students buy a second slice. Sometimes the cafeteria even runs out of pizza on pizza day. Students really like pizza.

Pizza can be one part of a healthy diet it is also a food that people likes to eat. If our school cafeteria served pizza every day, students might be healthier. They certainly would be happier!

Remember: Use this strategy in **your own writing**

Now go back to Luke's work on page 210 in the Student Edition.

Using a Rubric

Use this rubric to assess Luke's persuasive essay on page 211 in your Student Edition.

Does the introduction state the writer's opinion clearly to the reader?

Is there a paragraph for each reason? Does the conclusion restate the opinion?

Does the writer use enough facts to back up each reason?

Does the writer include only facts and details that support the opinion?

Do the subject and verb in each sentence agree?

your own writing

Save this rubric. Use it to check your own writing.

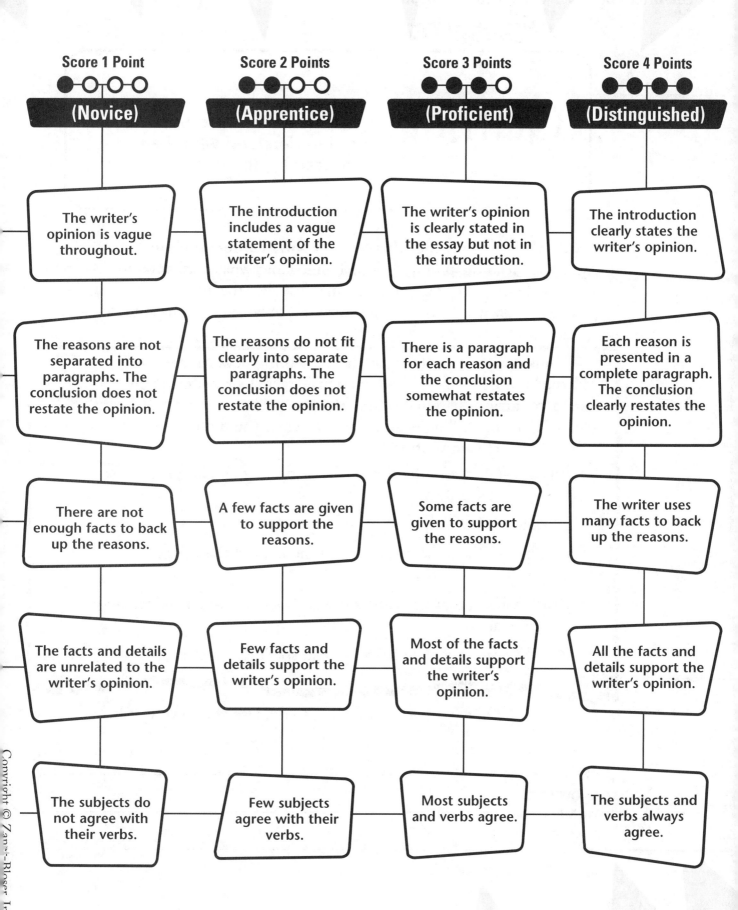

Score 1 Point (Novice)	Score 2 Points (Apprentice)	Score 3 Points (Proficient)	Score 4 Points (Distinguished)
The writer's opinion is vague throughout.	The introduction includes a vague statement of the writer's opinion.	The writer's opinion is clearly stated in the essay but not in the introduction.	The introduction clearly states the writer's opinion.
The reasons are not separated into paragraphs. The conclusion does not restate the opinion.	The reasons do not fit clearly into separate paragraphs. The conclusion does not restate the opinion.	There is a paragraph for each reason and the conclusion somewhat restates the opinion.	Each reason is presented in a complete paragraph. The conclusion clearly restates the opinion.
There are not enough facts to back up the reasons.	A few facts are given to support the reasons.	Some facts are given to support the reasons.	The writer uses many facts to back up the reasons.
The facts and details are unrelated to the writer's opinion.	Few facts and details support the writer's opinion.	Most of the facts and details support the writer's opinion.	All the facts and details support the writer's opinion.
The subjects do not agree with their verbs.	Few subjects agree with their verbs.	Most subjects and verbs agree.	The subjects and verbs always agree.

Prewriting

Gather

Read the writing prompt. Make sure I understand what I am supposed to do.

Now it's time to practice this strategy with a different topic. Carefully read the prompt below. Think about what it asks you to do. Circle the part of the prompt that describes the Task. Then circle the key words that tell you the kind of writing you need to do. Draw a box around the Scoring Guide.

> Think about a time that you did something new. Maybe you learned to ride a bike, played in a music recital, or visited a new state, country, or national landmark.
>
> Write a story telling what happened when you did this new thing. Be sure your writing
>
> • gets the audience's attention at the beginning and keeps it throughout the story.
>
> • tells the events in the order they happen.
>
> • includes details to help your reader picture the characters and events.
>
> • clearly tells who or what the story is about and when and where it takes place.
>
> • uses the conventions of language and spelling correctly.

Tell what the test asks you to do. Use your own words.

_____

_____

_____

 Now go back to Lucy's work on page 224 in the Student Edition.

Prewriting

Gather and Organize

Choose a graphic organizer. Use it to organize my ideas.
Check my graphic organizer against the Scoring Guide.

your own
writing

Now it's time to practice these strategies. Go back and reread the writing prompt on page 126 of this book. Then fill in the story map to plan your story.

Setting:	When? Where?

Characters:

Beginning:

Middle:

End:

Now check your story map against the Scoring Guide on page 126 in this book. Make any changes that will make your story better.

Now go back to Lucy's work on page 228 in the Student Edition.

Drafting

Write

Use my story map to write a good beginning, middle, and end.

your own writing

Now it's your turn to practice this strategy. Look back at the story map you made to plan your story about a time you did something new. Use your story map to draft your story. Make sure your beginning tells readers when and where your story takes place. Make sure your story has a clear beginning, middle, and end.

_____

_____

_____

_____

_____

_____

_____

_____

_____

_____

Drafting

Write

Use my story map to write a story with a good beginning, middle, and end.

_____
_____
_____
_____
_____
_____
_____
_____
_____
_____
_____
_____
_____

 RETURN Now go back to Lucy's work on page 230 in the Student Edition.

Revising

Elaborate

Check what I have written against the Scoring Guide. Add any missing details.

Now it's your turn to practice this strategy. The writer of the following passage needs more details to tell where, when, and why some events in the story took place.

Read the details in the box. Decide where each detail could be added to the draft. For each place in the draft where you see the symbol ∧, copy the detail that helps clarify when, where, or why the events take place.

to walk Scooter, our dog	to see if it was done	minutes later

We rinsed off the vegetables again and started to boil the

spaghetti. the timer went off, and Dad drained the

spaghetti. Then he poured it onto our plates. Before calling

Mom to dinner, he went out. While he was gone, I decided

to test the spaghetti. I thought I would check up on Dad

to see if he had done it right. I remember Billy telling me

how his mom tests it. Billy said his mom throws the spaghetti

against the refrigerator. If the noodles stick to the door,

they are done. I picked up a plate and tossed the

spaghetti against the fridge.

Remember: Use this strategy in *your own writing*

RETURN Now go back to Lucy's work on page 231 in the Student Edition.

Revising

Clarify

Check what I have written against the Scoring Guide. Make sure everything is clear.

Now it's your turn to practice this strategy. Read part of one writer's draft about a time when he helped his dad make dinner. The writer needs to clearly tell when his story takes place. He also needs to make the main characters in the story more clear. On the lines below, rewrite the paragraph including more details to help the readers.

One of my best memories is when we made dinner together. We decided to make spaghetti with vegetables. We wanted her favorite meal to be a surprise.

_____

_____

_____

_____

_____

_____

_____

_____

Remember: Use this strategy in **your own writing**

Now go back to Lucy's work on page 232 in the Student Edition.

Editing

⊐ Indent.	ℓ Take out something.
≡ Make a capital.	⊙ Add a period.
/ Make a small letter.	⌗ New paragraph
∧ Add something.	SP Spelling error

Proofread

Check that I have used correct grammar, capitalization, punctuation, and spelling.

Now it's time for you to practice this strategy. Below is a revised story about the first time the writer helped cook dinner. Use the proofreading marks to correct any errors in grammar, capitalization, punctuation, and spelling.

One "first" that comes to my mind is the first time I cooked dinner. I didn't really cook all alone. I was just helping Dad. We decided to make spaghetti with vegetables. We wanted to surprise Mom with her favorite meal.

The first thing we did was wash our hands. Dad asked me what vegetables I wanted to use. Then he cut them into bite size peices.

Dad told me to rinse the vegetables off in the sink while he went to check on the baby. I started rinsing the celery and peppers. When I was done, I stacked a nice pile of vegetables into a big pyramid.

Suddenly the phone rang. It was my friend Billy calling about the math homework. I didn't look behind me as I talked to Billy.

Then i heard a soft thud and turned to see Bitsy, our cat. She had knocked a piece of carrot on the floor and was trying to roll it around with his nose. Dads eyes got big as he came back in the room. Bitsy had knocked over the whole pyramid, and vegetables were all over the floor.

We rinsed off the vegetables again and started to boil the spaghetti. the timer went off and Dad drained the spaghetti. Then he poured it onto our plates. Before calling Mom to dinner, he went out. While he was gone, I decided to test the spaghetti. I thought I would check up on Dad to see if he had done it right. I remember Billy telling me how his mom tests it. Billy said his mom throws the spaghetti against the refrigerator. If the noodles stick to the door, they are done. I picked up a plate and tossed the spaghetti against the fridge.

Just at that moment, Dad walked in the door with Scooter. "What are you doing!" he yelled. I told him I was checking the noodles, just like Billy's mom does. "Not a whole plate," he said. "Im sure she meant to just check one noodle!" Oops.

Then Mom came downstairs. She was pleased we were making her favorite meal, until she saw the mess I made. She asked how the sauce was coming. Dad and I just looked at each other. Sauce? Mom explained that she always starts the sauce hours before everything else. We thought she just opened a jar.

"Why don't you guys clean up this mess," Mom said. "In the meantime, I'll order a pizza."

Remember:
Use this strategy in
your own writing

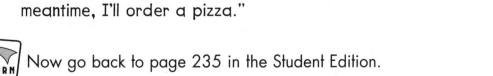
Now go back to page 235 in the Student Edition.

Using a Rubric

This rubric for narrative writing was made from the Scoring Guide on page 215 in the Student Edition.

Does the introduction get the reader's attention? Does the story hold the reader's attention throughout?

Are the events told in the order they happened?

Are details included to help the reader picture the characters and events?

Is it clear who or what the story is about and when and where it takes place?

your own writing

Save this rubric. Use it to check your own writing.

Are correct grammar, usage, mechanics, and spelling used?

Score 1 Point
● ○ ○ ○
(Novice)

Score 2 Points
● ● ○ ○
(Apprentice)

Score 3 Points
● ● ● ○
(Proficient)

Score 4 Points
● ● ● ●
(Distinguished)

The introduction does not get the reader's attention, and the story does not hold it.

The story has an interesting introduction, but it does not hold the reader's attention throughout.

The story has an interesting introduction and holds the reader's attention in most parts.

The story has a very interesting introduction and holds the reader's attention throughout.

The events are told out of order.

Some events are told in order.

Most events are told in order.

All events are told in order.

No details are included to help the reader picture characters and events.

Few details are included to help the reader picture characters and events.

Some details are included to help the reader picture characters and events.

Many details are included to help the reader picture characters and events.

It is not clear who or what the story is about or where and when it takes place.

The story has some clear parts—for example, who or what the story is about, and some unclear parts—for example, where and when the story takes place.

Most of the parts of the story are clear.

It is very clear who and what the story is about and where and when it takes place.

There are many errors with grammar, usage, mechanics, and spelling.

There are some errors with grammar, usage, mechanics, and spelling.

There are few errors with grammar, usage, mechanics, and spelling.

Grammar, usage, mechanics, and spelling are correct.